The

Space

Economy

Book Zero of the Space Economy Series

By George S. Pullen and Samson Williams

Dedication

Samson Williams - Dedicated to all the men and women who so bravely venture into the Expanse.

George S. Pullen - Dedicated to my wife, children, parents, and friends without whose support I could not have done this.

GEORGE PULLEN'S OFFICIAL DISCLAIMER

"The Space Economy" does not relate to Mr. Pullen's official position with the United States Government. In accordance with 18 U.S.C. § 209 the teaching, speaking and writing around this book takes place outside his official government position and is not undertaken as part of his service in the executive branch. Additionally, following 5 C.F.R § 5101.103(c) prior outside activity approval includes agreements related to Milky Way Economy, LLC and its joint publishing, distribution and other agreements concerning the book. Further, he was not invited by a related party to enter into these agreements and was undertaken based on personal interest, research and expertise in the topic. Members of the public should know clearly that this is not a product of any agency's official speech or official position but undertaken as the exercise of Mr. Pullen's free speech as a citizen of the United States.

Moreover, the content of the book does not relate to any of his official duties because it is not a topic of his presently assigned duties as senior economist at the U.S. Commodity Futures Trading Commission (CFTC) or any of his duties within the past year. The information conveyed through the writing also does not draw upon nonpublic CFTC information or substantially on ideas or official data that are nonpublic information as defined in 5 C.F.R § 2635.703(b).

The views expressed by Mr. Pullen are made in his personal capacity and are based upon his personal research and independent understanding of Space Economics, and does not necessarily represent the views of the CFTC, its Commissioners, or the United States government. Nor does his personal views constitute or imply any CFTC or United States Government endorsement of, or preferential treatment to ward, any non-federal entity.

About George Pullen

Chief Space Economist and Co-Host, The Space Economy - Your Destination for the Business of Space Ⓣᴹ

Adjunct Professor, University of New Hampshire School of Law - Blockchain Program, Economics and Social Impact of Technology

Guest Lecturer, Eisenhower School, USA War College - Rare Earths, Blockchain, Derivatives, Commodity Markets and Financial Analysis

Subject Matter Expert and Risk Advisor, Global Association of Risk Professionals - Energy Markets, Risk Analysis, Financial Instruments and Valuation & Structuring

Partner and Chief Economist, Milky Way Economy, LLC. - Forecasting and Strategy for the 5th IR of the Space Economy

Chief Space Economist

George is a free-market economist, with twenty years of experience as a strategic, analytical, problem solver. Prior to launching the Milky Way Economy, LLC, he learned his craft serving as an executive as a banker, broker, hedge fund trader, economist and lecturer. His areas of market expertise, research, and publishing include: healthcare, energy, blockchain, rare earths, derivatives, trading, defense innovation, AI/ML, risk modeling, crowdfunding and Space Economics. For the last decade has been refining his economic philosophies as Senior Economist at the US Commodity Futures Trading Commission. He is driven by a curiosity and passion for convergence, connecting people and ideas across diverse disciplines and finding new questions that need answers. George splits his time between DC and Maine. He was once and is always a US Marine and is an alumni of UMaine and Johns Hopkins. He has a wonderful wife and four beautiful kids.

Follow George on Twitter/Instagram @MilkyWayEconomy, catch his newest episodes and analysis on Space Channel or reach out to him on LinkedIn to follow the latest insights in his economic, finance and market Space research.

SAMSON WILLIAMS' OFFICIAL DISCLAIMER

If Space is colonized, someone will have to kill the Masters.

About Samson Williams

Co-Host, The Space Economy Boldly going where no anthropologist has gone before.

Adjunct Professor, University of New Hampshire School of Law - Blockchain, Cryptocurrency & Law Program.

Adjunct Professor, Columbia University - Blockchain, AI, Cryptocurrencies, FinTech, Machine Learning & the Space Economy.

Co-Founder Milky Way Economy, LLC. Monetizing the data of the Space Economy.

President, Crowdfunding Professionals Association. Because customers have more money than investors.

Anthropologist

Samson is a classically trained anthropologist, finance and public health expert who advises Fortune 100 companies, Executives and startups in Dubai, UAE, Washington, DC and Dublin, Ireland. Samson learned his craft as Emergency Manager at Fannie Mae 2008 - 2016 and has since gone on to be a leading advisor to banks and financial institutions in the Dubai / Middle East North Africa region. Samson's focus is helping firms understand the latest human trends in fintech, digital transformation, the Space Economy and Low Earth Orbit entrepreneurship so that they can make profitable decisions for their bottom lines. As part of this passion for the next steps in Human evolution and cultural development, Samson joined the Space Channel as Head of Anthropology and co-host of The Space Economy Show in March 2020. In this phase of his career he is focused on making Space exploration possible for everyone. You can follow Samson on Twitter/Instagram @HustleFundBaby or reach out to him on LinkedIn to follow the latest insights in his academic and market research.

In Space there is nothing more precious than water...except maybe data.

The Internet Economy will be to the Space Economy what the Earth is to the Sun. Tiny by comparison.

By The Numbers - The Space Economy

$400B

The value of the Space Economy in the year 2020.

$4Trillion+

The value of the Space Economy by the 2040s.

1 Million

Number of Humans living on Mars by 2050, per Elon Musk, the Milky Way Galaxy's first Quadrillionaire.

Questions?

Tweet us @MilkyWayEconomy #SpaceEconomy

Table of Contents

DEDICATION   3

GEORGE PULLEN'S OFFICIAL DISCLAIMER   4

ABOUT GEORGE PULLEN   5

SAMSON WILLIAMS' OFFICIAL DISCLAIMER   6

ABOUT SAMSON WILLIAMS   7

FOREWORD   14

INTRODUCTION   16

PREFACE - INDUSTRY VS ECONOMY   18

AUGUST 2021 UPDATE   19

CHAPTER 1 - WHAT HAPPENS IN SPACE STAYS ON THE GROUND   20

CHAPTER 2 - INTRO TO THE SPACE ECONOMY: HOW DID WE GET HERE?   22

CHAPTER 3 - SPACE ECONOMICS AS A FIELD OF STUDY   26

CHAPTER 4 - SPACE MONEY   32

CHAPTER 5 - LAUNCH COSTS AND ROCKETS   42

CHAPTER 6 - SPACE STATIONS   52

CHAPTER 7 – SPACE TOURISM   55

CHAPTER 8 - MAINTENANCE IN SPACE (AKA 3D PRINTING)   57

CHAPTER 9 - SPACE DATA   59

CHAPTER 10 - SPACE CONSTRUCTION   61

CHAPTER 11 - SPACE ECONOMY JOBS EARTHSIDE   64

CHAPTER 12 - SPACE POLITICS   65

CHAPTER 12A - WAR AS AN EXTENSION OF POLITICS.   69

CHAPTER 12B - CORPORATE SPACE POLITICS   71

CHAPTER 12C - MOON AND MARS SPACE POLITICS   72

CHAPTER 12D - SCIENCE NOT SPACE POLITICS   73

CHAPTER 12E - SPACE ESPIONAGE   75

CHAPTER 13 - SPACE RACE "3.0"   77

LESSONS FROM THE FIRST INDUSTRIAL REVOLUTION (1760- 1840)   77

AND SPACE COAL   77

LESSONS FROM THE SECOND INDUSTRIAL REVOLUTION (1860-1910)   80

CHAPTER 14 - SPACE LESSONS FROM THE 3RD IR (1950-1990)   84

CORONAVIRUS UPDATE   86

CHAPTER 15 - GPS AND GNSS   88

CHAPTER 16 - THE FOURTH IR IS HAPPENING TODAY   90

CHAPTER 17 - 4IR ARTIFICIAL INTELLIGENCE   91

CHAPTER 18 - 4IR CLOUD COMPUTING   92

CHAPTER 19 - 4IR GENETICS AND HEALTHCARE   93

CHAPTER 20 – 5TH IR = SPACE   96

DATA IS THE NEW OIL. DATA IS GOLD.   96

CHAPTER 21 - NEW ENERGY   98

CHAPTER 22 - FAR AND AWAY THE COLONIZATION OF SPACE   101

CHAPTER 23 - SPACE FORCE   103

CHAPTER 24 - SPACE FORCE AND 22ND CENTURY WARFARE   108

CHAPTER 25 - DE-RISKING OFF WORLD VENTURES & SPACE INSURANCE   111

CHAPTER 26 - WHAT IS THE SPACE ECONOMY ABOUT?   117

CHAPTER 27 - DRONES IN SPACE   120

CHAPTER 28 - MANUFACTURING IN SPACE: ZBLAN, MADE IN SPACE™   121

CHAPTER 29 - 4D PRINTING   123

CHAPTER 30 - RECYCLING, SOLAR & CIRCULAR ECONOMIES   124

CHAPTER 31 - SPACE TRASH   126

CHAPTER 32 - COMMODITY TRADING ON THE MOON   128

CHAPTER 33 - RARE EARTHS 101   130

CHAPTER 34 - SPACE MINING   132

CHAPTER 35 - NATIONAL MOON BASES   135

CHAPTER 36 - MOON MISSION THE SEQUEL - THIS TIME IT'S PERSONAL   137

CHAPTER 36A - RUSSIA ZVEZDA TWO   138

CHAPTER 37 - EUROPEAN UNION MOON VILLAGE(S)   140

CHAPTER 38 – CHINA'S MOON BASE   142

CHAPTER 39 – MOON BASE INDIA   143

CHAPTER 40 – MOON BASE JAPAN   144

CHAPTER 41 – MOON BASE *NEW JERUSALEM*   147

CHAPTER 42 – DUBAI LUNA   149

CHAPTER 43 – LUNA LUXEMBOURG   150

CHAPTER 44 – NORTH NIGERIA   151

CHAPTER 45 - FARMTECH IN SPACE   152

CHAPTER 46 - URBAN FARMING AND CRISPR LESSONS   156

CHAPTER 47 - CIRCULAR ECONOMICS OF SPACE PEE   160

CHAPTER 48 - ZERO-G FISH FARMS   162

CHAPTER 49 - THE ANATOMY OF A $1000 BURGER   164

CHAPTER 50 - BEER'S FINAL FRONTIER   168

CHAPTER 51 - CURRENT STATE OF THE SPACE ECONOMY AND AI   170

CHAPTER 52 - PREDICTIONS FOR THE SPACE ECONOMY 2030 TO 2100   171

PROLOG – BOOK IV, AI & THE SPACE ECONOMY   173

Foreword
By George Pullen, Space Economist

(**Note** – This was actually an email George sent Samson on Sat, Dec 26, 2020 at 1:59 PM george pullen gp@georgepullen.com wrote... We share it here for two reasons: **1)** It conveys George's unbridled passion for The Space Economy and really sets the stage for understanding the Space Economy as a stand-alone subject **2)** Samson does the last edits and so George doesn't know I copied and pasted his email.)

The Fifth Industrial Revolution [#5IR] - more popularly referenced as the Space Economy - will be launched off the shoulders of the amazing transformations that surround us today in the 4IR.

Yes, we are currently in an industrial revolution. You can either believe it or wait for an economist to tell you tomorrow what your experience, intuition and insight are all already telling you today. The four dragons of the 4IR, like the famous Chinese fairy tale, each represent rivers of change and opportunity. If you're not familiar the dragons names are Long, Yellow, Black and Pearl. A big fan of art and tech (STEAM) I'd encourage you to search out the many versions of the story and artistry available around it.

Anyway, the Long is advancements in longevity in medical and healthcare advances, this includes genetics, digital health, telemedicine and so many more to improve and extend life. The Yellow is revolution in money and electronic ledgers like blockchain but also the changing ways the meaning of value is collected, stored and exchanged. We've come a long way from passing around yellow rock in the shape of circles, or at least we like to think so. The Black is sea shifts in energy that, like prior industrial revolutions with coal and oil, with green energy, nuclear, fusion, solar are mixed with socioeconomic factors now called ESGs[1].

The final dragon is Pearl, which is big tech and big data that is an advancement by itself. The dragon includes advanced manufacturing and 3D-printing but also, like its siblings, often mixes and adds strength and momentum to the changes brought by each of the other dragons.

With that same picture in mind we also are living in a soon-to-be Post Covid19 world, with the reality that small and medium size businesses are getting crushed due to the Coronavirus Pandemic. This is true for startups, to generational family businesses, from new technology innovators, to neighborhood deli & bakers, and from Maine to Hawaii.

What's coming next in the Trillion-dollar Space Economy is going to be amazing and the greatest feat and opportunity of our species. That's why I started taking about #thespaceeconomy and winning you over as far back as 2019 after the Avantpay epiphany moment.

But entrepreneurship and helping those who need help means being able to pivot at light speed. To get to the 5th Industrial Revolution we are imagining we have to make sure we are not just working hard and remaining cognizant of the changes…but also bringing as many along with us as possible. If we've learned nothing in 2020 it's that humans are social beings and personally, I don't want to be alone on the Moon or Mars.

So, together with Brite.us we'll be able to help not only share awareness of the Space Economy but also spread awareness to Space and Earth businesses about the funding opportunities provided by investment crowdfunding. By helping startups and businesses raise money with Brite.us, we guarantee that we won't be alone on the Moon. Let's not be awesome alone but bring as many people along with us as possible. Right?

---

[1] ESG stands for Environmental, Social, and Governance. Investors are increasingly applying these non-financial factors as part of their analysis process to identify material risks and growth opportunities.

-GSP-

Introduction
By Samson Williams, Anthropologist

In truth I wanted to name the title of this book, *"Generational Wealth & The Space Economy"*. As when I speak of the Space Economy, I'm really looking into the future of generational wealth creation. The Space Economy and Space in general will be the 5th Industrial Revolution's version of Silicon Valley. Why this is important for you and me to be aware of is simple, money. Lots and lots of [2]money.

- **The first Quadrillionaire will be a Space based business.** Meaning a business based in Space. Probably the Moon. Probably not "American" as we understand the nationality today.
- **She will be the richest person in the Milky Way Galaxy.** Space will be woman owned for so many reasons. That by itself will be a cultural shock that will rewrite gender roles and be more disruptive than the 15th and 19th Amendment and desegregation.
- **Historically, Trickle Down Economics (TDE) has only worked when you're already on your knees.** In Space though, when the new wealth class has generational spanning wealth, TDE looks a lot like UBI (Universal Basic Income).

Yes, that all sounds fanciful and futuristic. Alas, we are living in the

---

[2] "Money' isn't the same in the Space Economy. I'm using the term loosely so the reader can appreciate the present understanding of "value" that we call money. For more information on what we mean by "money" in the Space Economy, checkout out Book I in the Space Economy Series, *"Blockchain & The Space Economy"*, specifically Chapters 7, 11 and 38.

future even today. Technology is advancing at such a pace that we will have permanent Human settlement on the Moon by 2030. "We" meaning Humanity, not the USA. I'm betting a China/Russia or UAE/Japan collaboration get there first. But that is a Space Race for another book. In the meantime, as Humanity reaches for the heavens the Space Economy will spawn an entirely Nouveau riche class of Space barons that will make Jeff Bezos empire look like a lego set and Oprah a beggar with a microphone.

As a Blexican from Texas for me the Space Economy is a wealth generating engine that all Black people, La Raza and people of Color need to be aware of. Black folks were denied access to the generational wealth that Silicon Valley spawn. To this day, Minorities constitute less than a satoshi of the millionaires that the Internet Economy spawn. Those early Internet pioneers, entrepreneurs, investors and Founders are today's Venture Capitalists and their kids will be Forbes 30 under 30, "self-made" billionaires, in this coming decade. However, compared to the unlimited wealth that the Space Economy will spawn, these folks will look like quaint, salt-of-the-earth, middle class Earthlings.

So, yes. The Space Economy exists. This book isn't going to tell you how to make a quadrillion dollar. But it is going to open your mind to the possibilities of doing just that.

Good luck. May the odds, algorithms and the gold pressed latinum forever be in your favor.

Samson

@HustleFundBaby

Preface - Industry vs Economy

Less than 7% of readers actually read entire books. So, we're putting the most important facts up front.[3] We get it, you're busy but you did buy our book and if you really need to know that much about The Space Economy, we have a very unreasonable hourly rate we'll happily charge you. So, as you prepare for your next happy hour or business meeting here is a quick and easy way to remember and position yourself as an expert on The Space Economy.

- **AOL, Comcast, Amazon, Sprint, Verizon** are all businesses who are part of the Internet *Industry.* Those businesses build the infrastructure and networks that make the World Wide Web work. They are in every sense of the word "Industry" players.
- **Influencers and TikTokers** are part of the Internet *Economy.* Influencers and TikTokers don't build the internet but they monetize their interactions on the internets. Hence why Influencers are part of the Internet Economy but not Industry players.

Space is very similar. There are many industry players, some more famous or well-known than others: SpaceX, OrbitFab, Blue Origins, OrbitsEdge, NASA, ESA, the UAE, etc… However, the Space Industry is not The Space Economy. Yes, the Industry players do play a role in the larger Space Economy, but they are not THE Space Economy. Which leads us to the question of, "Who are the influencers and TikTokers of Space that make up

---

[3] Minus the easter eggs we've placed in the book for a wallet address with a surprise in it. But who reads footnotes?

The Space Economy?"

Elon is one of the more well-known ones, as is Milky Way Economy. But there are literally tens of thousands of businesses (and industries) that come together to form The Space Economy. So, if anyone ever says that there is no way that the Space *Industry* is worth $3Trillion dollars. Smile and agree because they are 100% correct.

August 2021 Update

Since we first published this book in 2020 a few things have happened in The Space Economy that have pushed its evolution even faster. So, some additional updates so that at any Congressional hearing or DC party you've got the right talking points.

The Space Economy

- Is worth $450B dollars as of 2021.

- The Space Economy will be worth $4T to $10T by 2040s.

- Is an International Space Race 2.0. With countries from the USA, UAE and Japan teaming up to race other counties like Saudi Arabia, Russia and China. This leg of the Space Race is truly an international team sport.

- You cannot be a Global Superpower if you are not also a Space power.

The Major Components of The Space Economy

1. **Upstream** (Launch & Spaceports)

2. **Instream** (Satellites & Space Stations)

3. **Downstream** (Data - Follow the money)

4. **Exploration** - To boldly go where no woman has gone before.

5. **The Role of Religion** in The Space Economy. (This is a theme we've never explored before. However, historically all great eras of

exploration and "colonization" have had the Church's blessings. As the Church has had a say in Space since March 1616, when the Catholic Church issued a prohibition against the Copernican theory of the earth's motion. Later, in 1633, this led to the Inquisition trial and condemnation of Galileo Galilei (1564-1642) as a suspected heretic, which generated a controversy that continues to our day.)

Chapter 1 - What Happens in Space Stays on the Ground

In order to grasp the implications of the Space Economy, we have to look at how the economics of life here on earth work. For instance, you would never say "The internet economy" when discussing Amazon, Apple, Google, or the majority of commerce that takes place on the World Wide Web (WWW). There is no "World Wide Web" economy. There is simply THE ECONOMY. Does the web play a role in THE ECONOMY? Considering that the only trillion-dollar companies are all web-based technology companies (Microsoft, Amazon, Google[4]) we'd have to say yes. The internet economy plays a role in THE ECONOMY, though we would never think to separate the two. It's just the economy.

Space is strikingly similar to the WWW. Or the world wide web is eerily similar to Space. They both exist. Business, science, politics, gambling, and other strategic and mundane things happen there. And those things that happen in Space (as with the things that happen in cyberspace) impact economies and conditions on the ground. In fact, what happens in Space (like the web) doesn't just affect what happens on the ground, but often enough determines and directs developments on the ground. What will the impact of the Space Economy be? From business, education, shipping, logistics, medical research, travel, tourism, health, medicine and politics, the Space Economy is the next frontier of human exploration and growth. Space is this generation's unexplored ocean. Bold explorers will venture into Space

---

[4] Depending on when you read this and how you want to interpret the minority public shares in circulation for PetroChina and Saudi Aramco, you could say that energy also makes this list of Trillion-dollar businesses. Don't worry, there will be plenty of energy business in the space economy and we will cover that more later.

and then on into Outer Space. Millions of star bound pioneers and pilgrims will follow.

In many respects, 2020 is like 1492. However, this time, when Columbus sails the ocean blue, she will do it on a BFR rocket. The "New World" she'll discover won't be what we now call the Americas but will instead be the space borne child of dreams, imagination, loss, and perseverance that Humanity births amongst the cosmos. Humanity is headed to the stars. Not just because we have an indomitable spirit to go where no woman has gone before; but because we also sorta ruined the planet. And we need a Plan(et) B.

Plan(et) B starts with the Space Economy. After all, Humanity's greatest feat isn't going to pay for itself.

Chapter 2 - Intro to The Space Economy: How Did We Get Here?

"Those things which I am saying now may be obscure, yet they will be made clearer in their proper place." - Nicolaus Copernicus

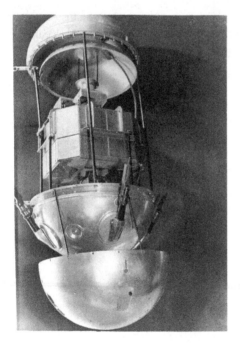

The Space Economy was created from a combination of Sci-Fi imagination and technological advancement, packaged together by economic incentives.

For many, the history of the Space Economy begins with a look back at the development of long-range rockets, namely the V-2, by the Nazis during World War II. Others might want to mark the beginnings of the Space Economy with the Soviet launch of Sputnik on October 4, 1957, or the first human to orbit Earth, Yuri Gagarin. More appealing to an American audience might be to look to the leap forward of the USA with Explorer 1, Alan Shepard, John Glenn, Buzz Aldrin, and Neil Armstrong when trying to pin down the beginnings of the Space Economy.

However, I present to you that the Space Economy was created when Claudius Ptolemy (A.D. 90-168) first set up models of the solar system with the sun, stars, and other planets revolving around the Earth. The change in the perception of celestial bodies from chaotic to geocentric was the first piece of the puzzle of building a Space Economy. A belief that Order exists is central to any human economic effort to manipulate it. Though space was still far from our grasp, we continued to look, and Azophi, Copernicus, and other notables grew our knowledge of the cosmos. It is also worth remembering that Billionaires (or their inflation-adjusted equivalents) have been investing in Space for millennia. They have long been patrons for early scientists and philosophers, and later funded Space exploration infrastructure.

This infrastructure pre-dates our modern efforts, and one such example of it can still be seen at the Birr Castle Leviathan great telescope, which was the largest in the world for over seven decades. These types of efforts brought science to the larger world, and helped scientists cultivate discovery, wonder, and innovation in their communities. They also allowed us to look up and realize nothing was looking back. Until we are shown otherwise, us "Terrains" are still very much the center of the economic galaxy, and Ptolemy was right!

[The Leviathan, Birr Castle]

Equally important to the birth of the Space Economy, was that our imagination grew to include technology not constrained by present realities here on Earth. This freedom of imagination facilitated the emergence of that most compelling genre of fiction, Sci-Fi, or Speculative Fiction. Some critics might rightly point out the three laws of one of the most famous Sci-Fi authors, Arthur C. Clarke who said, "any sufficiently advanced technology is indistinguishable from magic." As such, drawing the line between a rocket to the Moon and a chariot that carries the Sun becomes an arbitrary place to separate myth, magic, and "sufficient" technology. However, I would offer to you that the distinction with Sci-Fi was its democratization and decentralized ability to spread thought, creativity, and seed action to a wide cross-section of humans who then thought, "Hey, maybe we could do that!"

Any list attempting to chronicle every Sci-Fi text is sure to leave many writers out. Too, the line tracing their works is most certainly not straight, but the progression from Lucian to Francis Godwin to Mary Shelley to Jules

Verne to H.G. Wells is clear. If you haven't read any of these authors' works, it almost goes without saying that they play an important part in getting us to Heinlein and Asimov.

To summarize no Star Trek, Star Wars, Halo, or Firefly no Space Economy.

To pull from the advanced AI knowledge of Agent Smith (a Matrix movie reference for those non-Sci-Fi enthusiasts), we humans are not actually mammals. We're not mammals because we fail to operate in equilibrium with our surrounding environment. Instead we multiply, consume every natural resource, and then spread to another area to survive. By no longer restricting consumption to Earth, we push our fragile form of life out into the harshness of Space for the purpose of diversified, new, and greater resources.

Our power to expand into new environments comes from the economic incentives that we put in place, which govern our society. The East India Company's colonization of the subcontinent of India, South East Asia, and Hong Kong teaches us a lot about how we transition from trade to conquest. Everything we humans hold of value here on Earth, from natural resources to real estate, can be found in *infinite supply* in Space. Infinite supplies mean insignificant material costs, just costs for energy, mining, manufacturing, and transportation.

What does infinite supply do to demand? An understanding of supply and demand is so critical a concept in economics we refer to it as the "Law of Supply and Demand." The availability of a product and interest for that product forms a relationship that determines a product's equilibrium price. Ceteris paribus[5] the higher the price a product is the less will be demanded

---

[5] Ceteris paribus is one of those terms economists use frequently which is simply Latin for "other things equal". It is a way for economists to simplify assumptions

of it. Similarly, the lower the price a product is the less will be supplied of it. Taken together supply and demand help markets discover the price of products for a market.

Extracting value from space, however, is not a task well suited for the government, which is the original proprietor of the technology to get us to space. Governments often operate outside of the law of supply and demand and that is why the commercialization of space is the natural next step in the Space Economy.

Our technology is pulled along on a string by our imagination, while economic incentives provide the fuel for the Space Economy.

Chapter 3 - Space Economics As A Field of Study

"Giveaway and money just don't make sense together in a sentence, just to be clear." -Arati Prabhakar, Former Director of DARPA-

Changing forces in the Space Industry have made the 2020s the most important period of time for the industry since its genesis. The past decade has been a tumultuous period for companies involved with Space. Space firms, compared to most other industries, willingly and uniquely position themselves to battle the forces of technology and science in a rapidly changing field. In addition to the regular organizational, financial and human stressors a firm must deal with, this battle to forge discovery into the manifestation of a machine that can pierce the veil of heaven, adds another,

---

when putting together models or making forecasts. Unlike physical scientists, economists do not need to run additional treatments on samples in the laboratory to change the conditions of experiments. This is likely a contributing factor to why other scientists often refer to economics as the "dismal science" but really the creative or imaginative or notional science would be just as accurate a description. Other scientists likely wish they could isolate multiple variables affecting dependent variables so easily.

arguably more challenging aspect to the Space Industry's already daunting but necessary work.

Some of the most prominent examples of these battles are the work of SpaceX, the advancement of satellites, and the creation of the Space Force. The efforts of SpaceX portend some major events in the future of the Space Economy. Established in 2002 by Elon Musk, engineer, entrepreneur and tech Billionaire, SpaceX has forged for itself both a unique path and cult following. It is not the oldest privately funded space launch firm looking to produce technologies and business operations that enable private citizens' access to space, but it is certainly the most famous. The prize for oldest privately funded launch firm actually goes to Blue Origin, which was founded in 2000 by another famous Billionaire, Jeff Bezos. Blue Origin has focused on a more traditional path of incremental developments and partnerships with existing industry leaders and government contractors to secure a spot in the aerospace and defense industry to fulfill their goals. The difference in perception and financial demand from the two firms could not be greater but they provide a window into the industry.

A Rising Tide Lifts All the Boats

Also important is, while often framed as an industry of fierce competitors, the Space Economy is also a place where a rising tide can lift all the boats. Unfortunately, this also means that challenges faced by one firm can be seen repeated throughout the economy until a technological, economic, or organizational solution is discovered. All participants in the Space Economy, from those founded by Billionaires to those coming out of garages or small industrial parks, must master aerospace, satellites, and advanced technology, while at the same time balancing a discussion of economic principles within their decision making.

The 1960s and the spectacular Space Race between the USA and the Soviet Union is the first example of the interaction between Space and economic attributes of an activity. What we saw unfold was the use of economic power to express a technological superiority in Space. The Cold War Space Race has been detailed in countless other books. To summarize, it can be thought of as an economic victory first, with the Soviet Union producing satellites and putting humans in orbit, followed closely afterwards with the USA's efforts to match and then pass those technologies with the Moon landing.

Space technology facilitated the powerful introduction of a new realm of potential for more efficient communications, new energy technologies, and advancements in information management. The implications for a new dimension of defensive, scientific, and commercial development and dominance was dramatic. The ambitions of that period are captured in the proposed programs for Space urged by NASA, developed under President Johnson, and submitted to the newly elected President Nixon in 1969. Some of the more notable initiatives outlined projects such as a manned mission to Mars, a permanent Moon base, 2 Space Stations, one in orbit around the Moon and another around Earth, and reusable space shuttles. At the time many looked upon these ambitious projects as not just possible but likely, and published papers at the time noting the seismic implication of a change in the economic model of widespread implementation, adoption, and further development of such technologies.

The Tide Can Also Go Out Just as Suddenly

Unfortunately, just like all boats can rise when buoyed by a single force, in this case the US government is behind nearly all spending, the tide can also go out and leave the boats high and dry. Thus, like so many world events, the war in Vietnam changed everything as it shifted the attention of the public away from Space, changing the tone of the nation, taking resources away from the economy, and ultimately leading to the deaths of 60,000 young USA servicemen and 8 servicewomen (plus over 3 Million Vietnamese and others). What started as attempts by France to maintain colonial power from a bygone era when faced with the threat of Communist rule, and the Eisenhower "domino theory's" influence, ultimately led to Kennedy and later Johnson's escalation, only to finally end thanks to Nixon. Over the nearly twenty-year period of 1955 to 1975, spending in Vietnam was approximately $168Billion, and the USA drafted over 2 Million soldiers. Instead of continuing a proxy war based on science, technology, and Space against the Communists, one that included plans for the aforementioned missions to Mars, lunar bases, and multiple Space stations, US Leadership opted for an actual war. During the same approximate period, the historical sum budget of NASA was just over $55 Billion, or less than one-third of the reported direct spending on the Vietnam War.

It's uncertain if most or all the people of Earth would currently be enjoying universal access to the new technologies that might have come out of lunar bases, multiple Space stations and manned missions to Mars in the 1970s and 1980s. We are nearly fifty years removed from the conflict, and only now beginning to put these plans back into motion. In considering the aforementioned new technologies brings up some interesting considerations for Sci-Fi, and a potential reboot of Sliders (great parallel universe/alternate timeline show from my childhood). These speculations, however, do not change the economic realities, politics, and demands facing the various constituencies engaging with the industry or the modern Space firm.

Economics as a Framework for Thinking

Economic principles and commercial Space must be embraced by the industry if viable firms are to continue in an increasingly demanding economic situation. The economy of the USA, and most of the World, has been expanding since the end of the Global Financial Crisis ("GFC") of

2008-2009. In this environment of ever-increasing growth and prosperity, it is easy to lose track of the economic underpinnings of the market, business, or individual firms. Economics is best applied to answer questions regarding what is produced, how organizations manage and implement technologies, and who they produce it all for. Economic models applied to these questions provide a framework for thinking about these questions, and although not necessarily the ultimate answer, it gives the benefits of an approach to problems in business with use of the scientific method.

The Space Economy and Space economics as a field of study, are terms used to ascribe the financial activities, business models and market dynamics of firms producing, consuming, and selling output into the Space Industry. This is to be considered distinct from the larger aerospace industry, because while many firms do compete in both fields; the Space Economy has reached (and if not yet it certainly will in the near future) a size where firms operating in it and having recognizable congruence between each other can benefit from a field of economic study devoted to them. As is natural when a new field develops, Space Economics will begin by organizing to focus on the unique attributes of businesses, consumers, and regulations in the industry. There are already numerous fields of study within economics to include: urban, development, health, and financial, and Space has now also reached a stage where it has its own specialized and focused analysis, papers, and theories. Focusing on the decision making of firms operating in the Space Economy involves the assessment of market conditions, risks, technologies, regulations, and government involvements, plus imagination and the models required for analysis of the business ramifications.

Space Economics is the study of how Space industry firms allocate scarce resources to create technology, advance scientific knowledge, and forge our future in humanity's Fifth Industrial Revolution in Space. Space Economics is also concerned with how the needs of governments, militaries, commercial enterprises, and other institutions are met in Space. As is part of all economic fields, the overarching context of limited resources (scarcity), constraints from technology or organizations, preferences of buyers, and supply chains are also critically important to Space Economics. Unlike other areas of daily life most people have a hard time "seeing" the Space Economy even though the goods and services of which it is comprised are part of almost every person's normal activities. However, while some of the major firms in the industry are household names like Boeing, Lockheed Martin, Northrop Grumman and SpaceX, many others are not, and even some that people might be familiar with like Dish Network, DirecTV, Garmin or SiriusXM are not normally thought of as firms in the Space industry. Also, it is important to note that even among well-known firms, their structure is often complex, involving multiple business lines both within the industry to include:

- satellite communications
- national security
- human spaceflight
- imagery data analysis
- plus, business lines that may be outside of Space

Due to the expenses, risks and historic contracting of the government for Space, it is interesting to note that while very large and integrated firms do dominate much of the conversation and business, there still exists a deep and wide collection of small and middle size enterprises. When competing in science, technology, and innovation, like we saw with the internet, bigger is not always better. Sometimes the key to success is the unrelenting commitment, thoughts and energies of a small group. Firms like NanoRacks, Ball Aerospace, Valt Enterprises, and Accion Systems all illustrate that hundreds of smaller companies, not household names, also make major contributions to the industry.

As you will see throughout the remainder of the book, we identify and describe basic principles of micro and macroeconomics and consider the particular details of Space Economy firms and the market as a whole now and in the near future. Understanding the overall functions of Space operations and an examination of how they apply in a market and corporate environment will aid in building the necessary tools to understand the specific economic functions and behaviors of firms, governments, and consumers. Identifying the functional dimensions of selected firms and describing the dynamics of the fast-changing market they operate in will help reveal the important economic elements of structure, value, and policy that must be considered.

Chapter 4 - Space Money

"263rd Ferengi Rule of Acquisition: Never allow doubt to tarnish your lust for latinum" -Quark, StarTrek, *Deep Space 9*

The modern-day Space Industry developed out of World War II when businesses found commercial uses for military rocketry and satellite technology. We don't have to look to Imperial Credits or Gold-Pressed Latinum to find space money. The Space Economy is estimated to be between $350 and $450Billion as of 2019, with several predictions for it to reach $2Trillion in the 2030s, and we forecast it likely to pass $4Trillion in the 2040s.

Space, as defined as the region 100km (62 miles) above the Earth and onward, is needless to say a vast area. With an area this large in play for future economic activities, it is easy to see why it will reach Trillions of dollars in value in the not too distant future. To understand the money currently being generated by space we must first outline what activities are currently taking place that are generating profits for Earther businesses. The first and most important of all of these is the satellite industry.

Satellites and Ham

The satellite industry is closely tied to, but separately accounted for from, the launch market (we will talk more about the launch market a bit later). The global satellite industry launched 75 satellites in 2017, 138 in 2018 (a record year), and 95 in 2019. These satellites serve a few purposes, including but not limited to: Earth observation, followed closely by defense, and last communications systems. Estimates put the number of new satellites over the 2020s conservatively at over 1,500, being led by efforts from the United States, China, Russia, France, and Japan.

The current industry is a far cry from how it all started when the first satellites were launched in 1957. Sputnik weighed only 83.6kg (184lbs) and used four radio antennas to send pulses back to Earth which could be picked up by ham radio operators. If you don't know what a ham radio operator is, it's likely you are not a Prepper, or you don't have a former Navy Shack Fist in your family. But let's take a minute to dig into it because an understanding of ham radio operators, amateur radio technology, and long-distance communication culture is important to an understanding of both Bitcoin and the Space Economy.

[Ham Radio parts now on ISS, photo courtesy of NASA]

A ham radio operator is an individual who runs an amateur radio for two-way communication on a radio frequency assigned by the government for non-commercial use using a unique call sign provided after licensure. Around the time of Sputnik there were approximately 160,000 ham radio operators, and today that number is over 700,000 in the United States.

Interestingly the principles for ham radio operators, crypto-anarchists, and the Space Economy have a lot in common.

First Principles	Ham Radio Operators	Crypto-Anarchists	Space Economy
Groupings	Public Service	Community Service	Govt+Private
Influence	Advocacy	Activism	Lobbying

Experience	Education	Education	Education
Tools	Technology	Technology	Technology
Affiliation	Membership	Reddit Groups	NASA T-Shirts
Profits	Hobby+	ICOs+Shitcoins	Trillions
Personality	Marlon Brando	Satoshi	Spock

The uniting themes of public service, advocacy, education, technology, and membership are not unfamiliar to the crypto-anarchists or Space Economy ethos.

Ham radio operators can use the moon to bounce signals, generally Morse code, from one location on Earth to another thousands of miles away. It's important to note that ham radio operators also sponsored the launch of dozens of satellites starting as far back as the 1970s, and even the ISS (International Space Station) includes repeaters and a radio location on board (NA1SS at 144.49).

Sputnik vs Explorer

Now back to the Soviet Sputnik program. The Soviet's next satellite, Sputnik 2, was launched later in 1957, and included a dog as a passenger, making it the first Earthling in Space. For those of you who are animal or dog lovers I will not ruin it for you but the mission didn't go well for the canine cosmonaut. The good news is that a few years later, in 1963, a French cat named Félicette not only journeyed to Space but also safely returned to Paris where she lived out her life. This reminds me that we will need to talk more about animals in space a bit later. In 1958 Explorer 1 was launched by the USA as an answer to the surprise aerospace accomplishments of the Soviets.

In Space, size matters, particularly when we talk about getting things 100km+ up; and it is worth pointing out that Sputnik 1 and Sputnik 2 at 83.6kg and 508.3kg (1,121lbs), respectively were far larger than the 13.37kg (30.8lbs) Explorer 1. This was not something covered by the national media at the time, as Explorer 1 was a huge political victory and source of national pride for the USA. It is most revealing to understand the leaps forward in technology these first satellites provided as political tools more than economic productions. These first satellites paved the way for our early political, economic, and social drive for a future in Space.

Douglas-RAND was the first American company to start earning Space Money. Project RAND, the forebearer of the modern company with the same name, was originally set up within the Douglas Aircraft Company at the request of the Airforce (which at the time was still part of the Army) to study and issue a report on the feasibility, engineering analysis, and possibilities of an "experimental world-circling spaceship." The report, issued in 1946, estimated that to design, construct, and launch a spaceship would cost $150,000,000, which in 2020 would be almost $2 Billion.

RAND played an enormous role in the early research, development, and policy formation around the Space Race (part 1). RANDs work with the Ampex Corporation is what led to the development of magnetic tape for data storage, the precursor to the hard drive, a technology needed for storing data on satellites between transmission to stations on Earth. Other early partners with the US government for space included, but were not limited to, companies like: Lockheed, RCA, Philco, the COMSAT corporation, Hughes Aircraft, AT&T, TRW, Curtis-Wright, Aerojet, ITT, and GE.

Space is not just big business but Serious business

Space is a serious business. The consequences for wrong assumptions, errors, and failing to acknowledge what we don't know are million if not billion-dollar decisions; that may even involve loss of human life. This is another of the major reasons that up until more recently Space has been the primary domain of governments, militaries, and large international companies. But what economics shows us is, given the right policies and incentives, technology will translate into new businesses, new industries, and encourage higher levels of production given time.

When discussing the serious business of Space and the potential problems a firm can face when operating in the domain what we are really doing is thinking about the risks and the costs associated with those risks. The first role of a firm or industry acknowledging, addressing, and planning for risks associated with its operations is to categorize their risks into categories. The Global Association of Risk Professionals (GARP) uses a well-established system of six distinct categories of risk each with further detailed sub-components. Those categories are: technology, governance, energy, operational, credit and market. While an exhaustive discussion of each of these categories and their sub-components is beyond the scope of this introductory book[6] it is easy to see how each of these categories adds unique and, often with the case of the Space industry and firms, significant additional costs associated with these risks.

In the years following Sputnik, over 6,000 satellites have been launched. The satellite industry supplies information to DoD, broadcasts live sporting events around the world, improves weather forecasts, and enables you to rely on the GPS in your phone for all your directions. Space Money has been made for the dozens of previous named firms and the subcontracting companies that rely on satellites in their business.

---

[6] Risk professionals and the Space Economy Book 7 of the Space Economy Series

50,000 Satellite Space Economy Future

As we mentioned earlier, the estimates for new satellites produced in the 2020s go from the somewhat conservative number of 1,500 but range to as high as nearly 50,000.

While some of these efforts are coming from government space and defense spending, the majority of those efforts are coming from Starlink, Lynk, OneWeb, Telesat, and Project Kuiper. This is between an 8x and 9x increase in total satellite activity beyond what has occurred during the entire previous 60 years.

One of these firms, Lynk, is using a new type of technology that can send text messages straight from satellites to traditional cell phones. The company based out of Virginia, USA says their technology could eat 5G's lunch[7]. Lynk is aiming at messaging services via nanosats (small satellites) in orbit, and thus far has been on pace to launch something they call the "cell-tower-in-space" with four such satellites currently in orbit. This is different from the Starlink SpaceX approach, at least for early stages before one is able to offer a more complete service, and this is a great example of how the Space Economy is large enough for many different new ideas. Starlink today is not using antennas on towers, but instead employs Lynk specific technology that allows for sending signals directly from space to phones. This innovation has several implications such as impacts online workers, materials for lines and contract costs to install micro cells on utility poles. Additionally, and perhaps less obvious, is certainly the technology's ability to increase phone coverage

---

[7] https://www.satellitetoday.com/innovation/2020/03/30/lynk-co-founder-says-satellite-to-cell-tech-will-be-bigger-than-5g/

in unwired parts of the world, generating tremendously positive social impact benefits. The other implication is that this direct signal technology provides a more secure solution when considering cybersecurity risk issues to the current communication network.

Interestingly, Lynk is not really a Starlink SpaceX competitor, which is a great illustration of how the Space Economy is large enough for an array of new ideas. The reason they are not competitors is mainly because the two companies are focusing on meeting different needs in the communications market. Starlink seeks to be the speed alternative, whereas Lynk's strategy is to be the "blank space provider" of coverage. The economics are very different between these two approaches and while both companies include clear social benefit goals to Wi-Fi and signal- poor areas of the globe, Lynk is aiming at a valuable proposition for security, reliability, and complete coverage as a service. Also worth noting, Lynk used SpaceX launch CRS-20 (Commercial Resupply Service 2020) for delivery of recent satellites.

All this activity in building satellites also requires the launch capabilities to get them into low earth orbit (LEO) and beyond. Much of the new attention to the Space Economy comes from an interest in LEO because, well, it is the closest portion of the solar system to Earth and as such it is the gateway to our push outward. LEO is most simply defined as the region from 100km to 2,000km from Earth, and is the region where satellite phones and GPS communications operate. The International Space Station (ISS) is also in LEO at about 400km (250mi), which means even a round trip is shorter than my drive one way from Maine to DC. Only two dozen humans have ever left LEO and all of them were part of the Apollo program of the late 1960s and early 1970s. All 550+/- humans ever in Space besides those 24 have done so in LEO.

In addition to LEO are two other regions where satellites are placed in Earth's orbit MEO (M-for medium) and GEO/GSO (Geosynchronous Equatorial and Geostationary orbits). MEO is the intermediate region of space around Earth, extending from beyond LEO to 35,786km. MEO is also home to communication and GPS satellites with the advantage of completing one revolution every 12hrs; providing slower angular rates, or mean motion, which permits for longer and more effective static positioning. It is for this reason (and without getting into the trigonometry of GPS or a refresher on calculating cosine) that MEO satellites can effectively work together and complement many LEO satellites. GEO is the farthest region away from Earth— while still in a regular orbit— and positions a satellite in the same position in the sky at all times. One of the large business uses for this type of orbit for a GEO satellite is to deliver satellite TV to cover a given subscription region of a nation on a constant basis.

For many of these potential satellite constellations, the answer to the dependence on launch for successful execution is vertical integration. Vertical integration is a familiar term to economists and management students, and the subject of many models looking at efficiency gains and case studies, but to put it simply, it is when a company owns its supply chain. Typically, companies might participate in only the production, distribution, or retail parts of a business. An example of this common business relationship between firms is when Bud brews the beer, independent distributors act as middle men, and your neighborhood bar sells you the beer. When a company is vertically integrated, it has a market role more similar to that of many electric utility companies. Electric utility companies often own generating units, transmission lines, and distribution lines, creating, transporting, and selling power to customers. Another example likely in your home is Netflix. The streaming service Netflix is a great example because after starting out in the home DVD delivery business, they moved to digital streaming. Netflix then grew their distributional reach and then instead of just distributing the TV shows and movies of others, they created their own original programming (Altered Carbon is amazing!). This is also very similar to both Starlink and Project Jupiter, who can, respectively, catch a ride on their vertically integrated supply chain with SpaceX and Blue Origin providing launch. A slightly different form of integration is horizontal integration in an industry, which is where a firm merges or acquires another company in the same production stage to grow market size, increase product differentiation, achieve economies of scale, and enter new markets. A good example of this integration strategy in the Space Economy is Maxar, which has brought together a series of companies to provide manufacturing of satellites, robot arms for NASA & ISS, Earth observation, and Space data analysis services. Strictly speaking, few large corporations are either a pure horizontally or vertically integrated firm; it is important to understand both concepts and the market power they create. Companies that manufacture, deliver, and lastly operate their own satellite constellation will not only have market power, but also huge amounts of political power in Space, but we will get to that in a few more chapters.

5G and Internet Speeds

The decrease in size and cost of parts, along with the increase in launch capabilities and investments, have enabled this increase in activity. The aim of many of these satellite companies is to create constellations (although I prefer "arrays" as I think constellations should be reserved for only truly heavenly bodies), that will require connections between hundreds or even thousands of individual satellites to compete with existing Earth-bound fiber optics networks. The goal of this type of system is to provide internet at speeds comparable to Earth, to leverage 5G C band, and/or to provide internet coverage to connect remote places on the planet. 5G C band is used for satellite downlinks to Earth stations for fixed satellite services (FSS) and in the USA is from 3.7GHz to 4.2GHz and is in a similar band for other nations communication spectrums.

Internet speeds comparable to Earth would create substitution threats in an industry. This would change the competitive structure of the market from the entry into the market of new competitors. This is likely to have effects on the profitability of existing firms, as consumers are provided with additional choice. For consumers, these choices will be based on how sticky the existing product is, i.e. do you bundle your internet, cable, mobile, or are you in a contract. The pricing for access to the satellite based alternatives will be first in the minds of consumers because, while the technology being used in this way might be novel, exciting, and interesting; unless you are someone who is a natural enthusiastic early adopter of tech you will care much more about price and performance.

While we have already discussed the consumer, market juxtaposed with the business market, particularly we are thinking about banks and high frequency traders at hedge funds, performance is everything. High frequency traders conduct trades on stocks, derivatives, bonds, and global currencies in fractions of a second. When your profits are based not on novel insightful research, balance sheet analysis, or guts but on being 10 millionths of a second faster than the other person you will pay a lot for an array based internet system that gives you information on prices in London, Chicago, Hong Kong, or New York before the next person. If this seems far-fetched keep in mind the important role Wall Street has played as earlier adopter and funding agent on everything from the telegraph, to the ticker (first for Gold prices in 1866 but later with Thomas Edison for stocks), telephone service, and electricity.

Chapter 5 - Launch Costs and Rockets

"Production is at least 1,000% harder than making one of something, at least 1,000 percent harder." -Elon Musk, President of SpaceX-

Satellites are a very important sector within the Space Economy. Let's journey further into the cosmos and extend our thinking a bit to explore what other activities are going to occur in the next few decades. It is important to keep in mind that launching more satellites is driving down the overall cost of getting into space. It used to cost $100,000+ to launch a kilogram of freight into space. SpaceX has pushed that cost down to near $1k per kilo. How did they do that? Economies of scale. The more flights into space, the cheaper space transportation, flight, and exploration becomes.

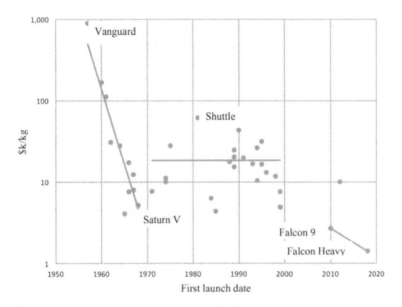

Graph courtesy of journal article: The Recent Large Reduction in Space Launch Cost

https://ttu-ir.tdl.org/bitstream/handle/2346/74082/ICES_2018_81.pdf?sequence=1]&isAllowed=y]

This table is with respect to launch costs into orbit but, to be thorough, the costs of delivering payloads to the ISS have also come down significantly with the Falcon 9+ Dragon being less than a quarter cost of the Shuttles.

Operation cost models are typically used to estimate Space launch systems operations costs. Launch system operations are defined as the business activities required to deliver a payload from a launch site on the Earth's surface to LEO. The operational costs are then generally assessed based on the breakdown of their work structure cost elements segments: program, vehicle, launch operations, and flight operations. The key here is that efficiencies are created in many of these areas with increased activity.

Experience Curve

Economists often look to model systems to determine what can be expected in the future, or to assist in decision making. While some of these techniques, methods, and analysis can look like mathematical witchcraft, others are based firmly within human experience. We learn by doing and, in general, get better with time and practice. The experience curve is generally considered more of a macroeconomics concept and, for this reason, when applied to microeconomics it is instead occasionally referred to as the industrial learning curve. No matter what name is used, the fundamental economic concept underpinning it is easily related to our own experiences.

This learning through experience is true for riding a bicycle, disassembling an M16A2 service rifle, and getting things into Space. Continuous improvements in the early aircraft industry and manufacturing, production, and performance advancements during the war time mass production period made this an expectation in forecasts. The experience curve showed that as total production (output of aircraft) increased, the costs and/or time requirement went down per additional batch of units.

We see this idea expressed in several other ways, such as 10,000 hours[8] of practice to reach mastery of a skill, and the encouragement of continuous efforts to improve. To translate this into the Space Economy, think about the cost of the experience gained by early aerospace engineers on the Space

---

[8] The idea of it taking 10,000 hours to master a subject is most commonly attributed to Gladwell from his 2008 book Outliers. Since its publishing several studies have provided differing amounts and methods for achieving mastery through repetition of a given subject but the idea still remains clear that as my mother taught me, "practice makes perfect."

program. There is a symbiotic relationship between the genius and the dreamer. The genius requires the necessary technical skills, knowledge, and proficiency to complete a task and the dreamer the passion and drive to do something over and over again. When combined the dreamer genius is a truly unstoppable force of both nature and economics.

The most famous early engineer is Wernher von Braun. "I aim at the stars" he is quoted as saying. "...but sometimes hit London," added by others. It is one of those cases where it is not entirely clear who was using whom. Things haven't changed. In much the same way von Braun's dreams of space and genius for rocketry were used during World War II still today dreamers and geniuses are thrilled to have government funding to go forth into Space, and the government is happy to have the technology it needs to exercise its sovereign power.

The industrial learning curve for spaceflight appears to be close to 0.9 and for orbital it appears closer to 0.75. What this means is that as volume doubles costs for spaceflight and orbital drop 10% and 25% respectively. To give these numbers some perspective, 70% is considered to be a very aggressive learning curve as most systems more heavily dependent on technology and machines have curves in the realm of 90% and labor dependent systems closer to a normal curve of 80%. For the space economy what this means is that as spaceflight increases and additional satellites are placed into orbital constellations we can expect what started out as the ideas of dreamers and geniuses will be diffused as efficiencies throughout the industrial cost structures for Space.

Closely related to the experience curve is Wright's Law, which states that the time or cost required to complete a task decreases as experience is gained, and that this occurs at a constant rate as cumulative output doubles. Another version of this experience curve is the Crawford model[9] which, when calculated, will yield slightly different results from Wright. Finally, all of this may seem similar to Moore's Law, and many people confuse the concepts, but Moore's law was a prediction (adjusted over time) suggesting that the speed of computer processors would double every two years. The increase in transistors in dense integrated circuits and the benefits it had on progress in the Space Economy should not be understated. It is often said that the iPhone has more processing power than the shuttles and those were several factors of sophistication ahead of the Apollo missions. So, no matter which model or law you prefer to help you conceptualize this phenomenon, the idea is the same: the more we do something, the better we big brained fragile mammals get at it.

Economies of Scale or the Halvening of Rocketry

What does the Space Economy look like when a gigafactory for rockets and spacecraft opens? It is important to understand the benefits of manufacturing a product hundreds of times over in comparison to making just one increase that product's value 1,000%. At the time of the writing of this book, early 2020, SpaceX was close to production of its 100th second stage engines for the Falcon 9. This brings us to one of the most important economic principles at work in Space, economies of scale! More and new opportunities that were previously too expensive are now being opened up because of economies of scale.

To appreciate the power of economies of scale requires a quick refresher from economics on variable and fixed costs in the long and short term. In the short term, you have a given amount of fixed costs that you have brought with you into the period or acquired during the period that can not change, plus you have variable costs that will change based on activity. In effect,

---

[9] The Crawford Mode or Unit Theory is where "learning in the production process, the cost of some doubled unit (say, unit #100) equals the cost of the undoubled unit (= unit #50) times the slope of the learning curve." WWII Airframe USAF learning curve theory study, 1947.

competitive and free markets industries will price a unit of output at the average total costs.

Launches	Fixed Costs ($Millions)	Total Variable Costs ($Millions)	Total Costs ($Millions)	Costs per Launch ($Millions)
50	10,000	1,500	11,500	230
100	10,000	3,000	13,000	130
200	10,000	6,000	16,000	80
400	10,000	12,000	22,000	55

(Note: this is for illustrative purposes only)

As shown above in this highly simplified table, you can see that fixed costs, spread over a larger number of launches, will bring down marginal costs per launch. Fixed costs associated with launch include things like: buildings large enough to stage in, vacuum autoclaves, operations, milling and welding exotic materials equipment, inspection sensors, and component testing devices. Variable costs per unit remain constant ($30 Million) in this table and would include such things as fuel costs, vehicle, and flight operations. In markets with perfect competition, note that Space is not one of those markets, a profit-maximizing firm will sell goods where market price is equal to its marginal cost and therefore is also equal to the marginal revenue of a good. In this example cost per launch would be the price to the market but because of a variety of factors, to include significant current barriers to entry for Space, this would not be the actual market price.

Given the above simplified example we can clearly see that launches, and presumably demand for them, have increased while at the same time costs have come down and this is a dichotomy between two ideas in economics.

On the one hand, improvements in technology drives costs down versus what we think of in economics as situations where greater demand can push prices up. This is another example of the magic of economics. Both concepts are correct and what is important to understand is that in every situation the size of the impact of these two forces will be different and it is the process of analyzing, modeling and forecasting that we are able to reasonably determine what to expect from these two opposing forces.

Long term, everything is a variable cost, so the average total costs can decrease. This decrease can come from a variety of sources, but they can broadly be viewed as a benefit of specialized technology, workforce & labor, and resource efficiencies. Efficiencies can come from many areas of the business. The best example of efficiencies in launch comes from SpaceX and its Falcon 9 rocket, which is designed exactly the same no matter the payload and incorporates reusable launch systems. This is very different from the traditional model used by ULA, a joint venture born through the combined efforts of Boeing and Lockheed, for the famous Delta IV Heavy and Atlas V. The beautiful thing about successful technology is it will quickly diffuse through a market and become commonplace, for example ULAs newest work developing the Vulcan Centaur features booster engines, avionics, and thrust structures that can detach, return and get reused.

Economies of scale lead us to our minimum efficient scale point, which is the largest amount of production possible at the lowest amount of cost when time is fixed. Below we illustrate the difference time can make on our hypotheticals, where technology transfer lowers fixed costs and the resulting total costs are shown to reduce even more. What we see in Year 10 is the dream of many in the Space industry, which is when a point is reached where the scale factor for cost of goods (launches) manufactured allows for more consistent gross margin.

Year	Launches	Fixed Costs ($Ms)	Total Variable Costs ($Ms)	Total Costs ($Millions)	Costs per Launch ($Ms)
1	50	10k	1,500	11,500	230
2	100	9k	2,500	11,500	115
5	200	6k	3,000	9,000	45
10	400	4k	4,000	8,000	20

(Note: this is for illustrative purposes only)

Space Sunk Costs and Horses

We cannot have a discussion about the Space Industry, rocket production, and technology innovation without discussing sunk costs. Sunk costs include things like research, development, machinery, and marketing. These expenses however are not disposable items for Space. Specifically, I am referring to the billions of dollars spent by NASA and the DoD to get Space technology to its current state of development. SpaceX early on was a major beneficiary of this R&D when the TR-106, or low-cost pintle engine, was developed by TRW under contract with NASA, and used in the early Merlin engine. We all stand on the shoulders of giants and sometimes those giants are categorized as sunk costs.

Now some economists might want to say that sunk costs are irrelevant to decision making because, by definition, they have already occurred and are being examined retrospectively. Or, to put it another way, sunk costs have already occurred in a previous period in time and should not have any impact on new decisions being made today. The other view of sunk costs, and the one favored by some behavioral economists, is that we are not rational efficient capitalist beasts, and instead of making decisions based on the future value of investments; we are strongly influenced by the emotional experiences we accumulate. The toughest part about learning to start thinking like an Economist is that you are still a human, and as such you know that we are certainly the accumulation of all our previous actions, thoughts, and feelings.

Another painful term to describe sunk costs is the Concorde Fallacy. This is particularly painful for followers of the aerospace industry, because the fifteen or twenty some odd Concordes built and flown represent one of the greatest engineering feats of aviation. Not only was the Concorde beautifully engineered and graceful, it was fast. All that engineering genius, beauty, and speed created pride. **Pride is a dangerous sunk cost.** The original program for the Concorde was projected to cost $90Million but ended up with a price tag estimated at $1.75Billion. This is another reason why sunk costs are also often referred to as "throwing good money after bad." Which is the concept by which individuals or firms waste money by spending additional money on something that is no good. Some examples of this include fixing an old car or loaning additional money to a firm that is already unable to make timely payments to creditors. However, on the plus side, if you want to see what something worth almost $2Billion looks like, a Concorde is on display at the Udvar-Hazy National Air and Space Museum just outside of Washington, DC.

To put this in better perspective, I referred to the Concorde as "fast", but to simply call it fast does little to adequately describe its superior performance. A "fast" human can run at 28mph for a brief period of time, while I would be happy to have my 10mph USMC 6min/mile time back. By comparison, a horse can almost double that speed at 55mph, and can comfortably hold a 15mph pace for hours. Your typical Boeing 737-800, which you have certainly flown on if you have done any sort of traveling, has a normal cruise speed of around 600mph at 35,000 feet. Next to it the Concorde is a race horse cruising at 1,340mph at 60,000 feet.

The Corinth of Space

All this talk of horses and the Concorde naturally leads us to consider the distance between cities in the Wild West and how it had as much to do with horses as it did proximity to resources. How long do you think your great^4 grandfather wanted to ride each day and sleep outside at the end of it? A well

trained and experienced horse might cover 40 or 50 miles in a day, but that varied greatly based on the terrain, this is in fact is the reason that the Romans built roads, to speed connectivity throughout their empire. How much different should we really expect the Human Space Empire of the future to be? Even at its closest distance, which is about 57Million km, Mars is not close and will take anywhere from six to nine months of travel time, depending on a variety of factors. Yes, someone is going to bring up 1G thrust and how it would take less than a week, and to them I will say, I look forward to seeing your design but this is like talking about the Concorde to a cowboy in the Wild West.

Our horses, as we push out to the Wild West of Space, are going to be the technological children and grandchildren of today's rocket work horses. With that in mind, and assuming we put 1Million people on Mars, it seems reasonable that many of them are also going to want a place or places to stop. The same way that towns sprung up on the Wild West routes and along Roman roads as places not only with resources but also offering relaxation and rest, so too will the new watering holes of Space. So what will be the places along the Via Appia or Fosse Way of Space? Potentially near-Earth objects (NEO) asteroids like the five that have been visited already by spacecraft.

Since we have already sent missions to asteroids, these are the likely places of commercial activity for asteroid mining. Once you have a mining operation in place, the additional facilities needed for a place for travelers to stop might be small in comparison. Now, it is worth pointing out that stopping and restarting a spacecraft is not as easy as a horse, and the location and orbits of the asteroids would be very important factors as well, but don't rule out a stopover at asteroid 101955 Bennu on your trip to Mars.

As we think about the future of Space opportunities and forecast what it could mean for the Space Economy, we will challenge you to not be linear in your thinking about this exponential industry. This is sure to be challenging as it is the easiest thing in the world to simply let our social, financial, or political biases shape our thoughts. New information that challenges what we already think we know is difficult to internalize, but to get past what is easy in this world and to what is possible for the future of Space is what we must do.

Chapter 6 - Space Stations

"One of the great revelations of the Space Age has been the perspective it has given humanity on ourselves. When we see the earth from space, we see ourselves as a whole. We see the unity and not the divisions. It is such a simple image with a compelling message. One planet. One human race." -

Steven Hawkins in his final message-

Space stations or Spaceports

The first thing that is natural for us to look at after satellites is a commercial space station, or if you prefer, spaceports. Most plans currently under consideration are for smaller operations relatively similar in size to what we currently have with the ISS, or have previously been done with the Skylab or Mir. The problem with these types of operations, and likely what any other space economist [I assume there are more or will be soon after reading this] would tell you, is that small station plans don't think large enough to take advantage of economies of scale.

The first space stations were launched by the Soviets who, having lost the race to the Moon, shifted resources, people, and scientific energy to long-duration space flight. On the heels of the USA moon missions, and only a decade from first sending humans to Space, the Soviets started the Salyut launches in April of 1971. The Soviets would go on to launch six more stations. From April of 1971 through May of 1982, the Soviets launched Salyuts 1-5, which were all able to receive crews to dock and support them for a brief period. Salyut 6 in 1977 was the breakthrough space station that first allowed for more extended living in Space. Building off the success of Salyuts 1-7, the Soviets put Mir into orbit in February of 1986.

Mir was huge by comparison to the earlier Salyuts. The Salyut space stations were all similar in size at only 20m in length, 4m in diameter, 100cu meters of interior space, and had a weight of 20 tons on Earth. Mir operated from 1986 to 2001 under first Soviet and later Russian control. Mir was assembled in space, the combination of a core and seven modules, over the course of multiple years. The modules ranged in size from 7m by 2.6m to 14.7m by 4.35m, giving Mir significantly greater interior space than any previous space station. Following the de-orbiting of Mir in 2001, one former director estimated that over 15 years the program (without launch costs) had been a

$4.2 Billion investment in development, assembly, and operations. $400 Million a year (in 2020 dollars) might seem like a lot but keep in mind that this included the development costs of: air supply systems, water purification technology, radiation shielding, and orbital solar energy systems. All of this technology having already been developed and, now decades later, improved upon; it is likely that the costs would be significantly less.

Not only have the costs of deploying and operating a facility in space come down but so have launch costs. As launch costs are now on pace to break below the $1,000/kg price, the potential for recreational space travel becomes accessible for those able to spend $250,000 on a one week trip. This is certainly not currently a business model in operation, but its future development is clear. Granted, this amount of money is still outside the reach and realm of possibility for the vast majority of the planet, but not outside the financial abilities of enough people to create a viable ecosystem of space tourism, and something for us to keep aiming for.

In the meantime, Virgin Galactic might be bringing tourists to Space as soon as late 2020. They have continued to make progress in recent years on plans to make sub-orbital Space open to tourism. Although some might not call this "real " Space we instead hold firm to the 100km Ka'rma'n line[10], and that height is crossed by the Virgin Galactic project. The VSS Unity has been on several test flights, and after a 15 year journey, an announcement on when commercial operations start looks imminent at the time of this book's writing. Many, including the 600+ people who have pre purchased seats for $250,000 each (these numbers being identical to the estimates above were

---

[10] The Ka'rma'n line is the altitude where air becomes space. It is 100km (about 62miles) high and is named for Theodore von Ka'ma'n who was a Hungarian American engineer who first calculated the altitude at which the atmosphere became too thin to support aerodynamic lift. It is commonly used to represent the border however others exist and the FAA, for example, uses 50miles to determine who it gives astronaut badges to. The line is also likely to separate the domain of the US Air Force from the Space Force.

only a happy coincidence), hope the time for them to touch Space could be coming soon. The lift mechanism of the spacecraft is different compared to others in the industry, and does not include launch capabilities that would allow for a trip to the ISS, or another future commercial spaceport, but that is not the current mission of the firm. Instead the focus is on commercialization through efficiently breaking the 100km line separating "air" from Space. The efficiency in the lift comes from SpaceShipTwo catching a ride to 50,000ft attached to another plane. From there, SpaceShipTwo uses rockets to propel it towards 100km, which it glides into and out of, for about 5min of weightlessness, and the selfie of a lifetime with you and the curvature of Earth against the void of space.

Chapter 7 – Space Tourism

Think about the competitive forces at play in this type of market servicing luxury space travel. At first a few enthusiasts may be happy for a simple up-and-down trip circulating the Earth a few times from a spacecraft, but that is not the true market for space tourism.

Luxury Space Hotels are next! Orion Span is one example of a New Space business looking at the future of Space Tourism. Twelve days on the proposed Orion Station will cost $9.5M. Not affordable for the average Earther, but it is in reach for the 100,000 hectomillionaires ($100 million or more in net worth). Even with only 3% taking the rocket ride on a spacecraft to a hotel, that's plenty of business and, more importantly to the rest of us, enough for innovation, experimentation and refinement.

The initial batch of space tourists took place from 2001-2009 and each paid $20-to-40Million (estimates vary) for their trip, so even before the first members of this next contingency take off, prices will have come down significantly. This market has the interest of Blue Origin, Virgin Atlantic, Bigelow Aerospace, Boeing, and SpaceX.

Also important to keep in mind is, besides just the "Scrooge McDuck" types, some of the 70 space agencies, of which only 8 have ever sent astronauts to the ISS, could lease out these new hotels for LEO research and operate a human spaceflight program modularly, affordably, and effectively.

Companies will push to offer more and additional services to space tourists. These tourists are the very definition of a captive market once aboard your spacecraft. Similar to when you are on a cruise ship, why not give travelers as many ways as possible to shop for overpriced merchandise, buy exotic drinks with umbrellas, and take excursions to beautiful locations where you spend half your time posing for selfies. Remember, much of the cost is getting your customers off the Earth. To make the rest of these profit opportunities possible, the Space industry will need a Spaceport.

Once at the spaceport it is reasonable to assume people would want to engage in all of the customary luxury activities of first-class travel: hotels, restaurants, spa, gambling, microbrew sampling, and posting your spacewalk to Instagram to make your friends hate-like your trip. It is also safe to say that similar to railroad resort towns, like Sun Valley, Idaho[11] that was established to increase ridership on the Union Pacific, out-of-this-world class resorts will be established to draw in tourists. While we are not sure what the first spaceport spa will look like, we are going on the record now to say that we are happy to help test and develop this concept with investors at any time. Although many of these services and experiences seem science fiction, their existence is a forgone conclusion because they create a perpetual motion machine of economics more powerful than even the endless printing of more fiat currency.

In addition to Space hospitality and tourism companies, private companies, colleges, and consortiums could gain access to space, thereby increasing research and development opportunities in medicine, optics, and energy. It is important to note that these individuals won't be called Space tourists. Rather, individuals who are headed to Space to engage in the business of Space will be referred to as Rick Tumilnson of Space Fund refers to them as, "Private Space Travelers". Private Space Travelers will be an entirely different and important segment of the commercialization of Space.

Chapter 8 - Maintenance in Space (aka 3D Printing)

Although it is possible that many of the jobs at a spaceport will be more affordably done by ground crews using drones or Robonaut-like machines working continuous 3-8hr shifts, 7 days a week, 365 days a year, there will still be many things we will only accept a human for, hence full-time spaceport staff will be required. The staff, just like the guests, will require living accommodations, food, water, energy, access to medical care,

---

[11] Sun Valley, Idaho was made famous by visits by Ernest Hemmingway and Hollywood elites recruited to visit by the railroad and resort business. It was also mentioned by Apollo 15 astronaut Jim Irwin when he stepped on the surface of the Moon comparing it to the slopes of Sun Valley he liked skiing.

entertainment, and more. Each of these requirements will lead to a still bigger spaceport. At first only a single commercial spacecraft company might construct such a facility. Again, since it is all about economies of scale, they are likely to provide docking privileges to spacecraft from other companies...at an appropriate fee. Probably based on the mass / size of the shuttle/ship.

Additional specialty industries are likely to also emerge from this growth naturally in Space activity. Maintenance, repairs, and construction will take place on a regular basis to maintain the spaceport. Again, since the primary cost associated with Space is breaking the Earth's gravity, you are not going to want to send Jane up every time you need more welding done. Instead she will live up there for a period of months. Think of this as similar to the way freight and cargo ships currently operate with crews that trade off every six months. Jane will have access to 3D-printers to manufacture large structures (habitats, ship frames, etc...) and smaller parts (bolts, filters, circuit boards, etc...) onsite for repairs instead of waiting for them to come up with the next group of space tourists or travelers.

As the number of spaceports grows, you will also need to think about services that connect tourists from one port to another and that connect mechanical, technical, or medical personnel from one station to the next, should they need to aid and assist each other. We have a model for this already on Earth. "Roughnecks", the ladies and gentlemen who do the hands-on work in the oil and gas industry, will be among Space's first working class astronauts. This was actually predicted in the movie Armageddon.

Chapter 9 - Space Data

In addition to the maintenance crews (and ultimately *government* safety inspectors. Hello Space OSHA), don't forget about all the data being collected on all these people in Space. From the point of view of evaluating the size of the Space Economy we cannot underestimate the value alone of all the data each of these space tourists, spaceport staff, and others will be generating. Each Space worker, tourist and resident will be outfitted with an IoT (Internet of Things) personal communications device colloquially called a "tapper".

A tapper is an Augmented Reality (AR) communications device. Think of it as a smartphone you can attach to your forearm, which allows you to interact with it either by voice or by tapping on the screen, even while on a spacewalk. Hence the name "tapper". Tappers exist for a simple, practical reason, spacesuit gloves are big. So, while wearing them on spacewalks you'll either talk to your AI-Virtual Assistant (don't worry Cortana, Alexa and Siri love the vacuum of space) or tap at the screen with your oversized gloves. While it is true that tappers do not presently exist, just a few years ago neither did Alexa, and now you can ask her to do all manners of things. For more information on the roll of tappers in Space, checkout B.V. Larson's series *Undying Mercenaries*. Yes, it is sci-fi. But, so too was your cell phone when the first version debuted on Star Trek, as a *communicator*.

These are just the tip of the Rocketship of examples of some of the new tech devices and apps that will contribute to the overall Space Economy. Keep in mind too, that tappers, (with or without AI assistance), will begin as subscription services but will ultimately be required by whichever insurance company underwrites the spaceport. Why does Google get into the business of Space insurance? Because they want ironclad access to the terabytes of data that visitors, residents and workers will be generating each second. If you think there is a lot of data on Earth Humans, just wait until you're required to wear a tracking device 24x7 to open airlocks, purchase food, turn on lights, control movies, and all the other things Humans like to do.

Realizing both the costs, primarily for cooling, and security issues with Earth based data centers; Space Data Centers will also be a huge business. Keep in mind that Space is cold relative to Earth, but also the temperature of a satellite or space station has a lot to do with its orbit. For example, a typical satellite in LEO can have any one of five different orbits: Sun synchronous orbit (SSO) dusk-dawn or midnight-noon, polar orbit, or elliptical orbit, and each has a different thermal profile. The duration of these orbits and the amount of time they are in a position to receive Sun-lit-phase heat versus eclipse-phase cold will depend on the type of orbit and altitude. The average range of the cold and hot temperatures in these orbits is between -250°C to 300°C (-418°F to 572°F). During periods of Sun, solar panels can collect energy that can be used later during extreme cold periods for unleashing supercomputer processing power with out of this world heat efficiency, technology pending. All this to say, keep an eye on the future of data generation in Space, as it will push the evolution and development of data centers and decentralized storage systems in Space. All of which will ultimately improve data center design, maintenance and capabilities on Earth, the Moon, Mars and beyond.

Chapter 10 - Space Construction

Another fantastic part of the economies of scale of a large spaceport is that with Space construction you are not fighting gravity. Sans the full-g effects of gravity, the strength of materials assembled in Space is different from the requirements here on Earth. In short, this means more "carpenters", "plumbers" and other skilled workers in Space. This may surprise some of you, but the future of Space is dominated by female "blue-collar", skilled workers. Also, since, as previously mentioned, launches are your primary cost it makes sense to use locally sourced materials. No, but seriously it begins to quickly make more sense to use natural resources from the Moon and asteroids as building materials for construction as economic activity picks up. *Keep in mind that while Earthbound Space workers will accept USD initially, as ecosystems and economies develop, they will pivot away from Earth-cash to blockchain based Elemental & PTEs tokens.*

The logic of large spaceports is even more clear when you think about the cube-square law. The cube-square law, brought to us by Galileo, himself a space nut, provides that as a shape grows in size its volume grows faster than its surface area. To put this into the context of a spaceport, think about the material and assembly costs for the outer structure, as we add additional 100 meter sections in each direction (Yes, we will not be using feet and inches in Space, just give it up already and go base10!) we are not simply adding 100meters of usable area to the spaceport we are adding 100m*100m*100m or 1million meters of additional volume to the spaceport. In addition to the cost of materials and assembly it is also important to consider the added cost effectiveness of radiation shielding applied to the outside surface that is far less than the interior volume. Also the interior volume of spaceports would be minimally impacted by the presence of support trusses because with no gravity support beams would not need to be every 5m apart like we see on Earth and this reduction in material would also result in cost savings for larger structures.

Submarines and Spacecrafts

Advanced nuclear submarine technology, manufacturing, and deployment is a great proxy for the required conditions for a nation also having the economic and manufacturing abilities to produce a spacecraft akin to those used in the retired NASA shuttle program from 1981-2011. Currently, six nations have nuclear submarines: USA, France, UK, India, Russia and China, plus the two programs of Argentina and Brazil, respectively, are ongoing. Much like the shuttle program, which began focused development and testing of the orbital maneuvering system (OMS) engines and other new technology as far back as the early 1970s, the long-term commitments to a space program are similar. The outlay and planning over decades of money, time, and technological investment constitute a sustained focus by nations looking to add capabilities to their power.

Interestingly, of aforementioned the list, only Argentina and Brazil have not achieved full launch capabilities. However, if their programs in nuclear submarines are any indication, we can anticipate them to also be major participants in the Space Economy. Notably, if not for the tragic 2003 Alcântara VLS accident and infamously on-again off-again relationships with the USA for technological partnerships, greatly complicated over concerns of ballistic missile development the Brazilian Space Agency (AEB) would already have full launch capabilities.

Noteworthy to keep in mind is that, to date, AEB has worked or is continuing efforts through several partnerships for joint technological development with Ukraine, India, Russia and China to expand their capabilities. The space program has achieved four successful launches of Earth-observation satellites built in a technology exchange with China. They have also enhanced suborbital rocketry abilities through partnership with Germany and constructed a GEO satellite jointly with support from Thales (a large aerospace firm based in Italy). Another major focus of the AEB efforts is to promote the launch of rockets from the Alcântara Launch Center (CLA). After the end of a joint partnership called Cyclone to develop CLA with Ukraine for commercial launches in 2015, Brazil has been working to establish mechanisms for a return to USA and Brazilian cooperation. As recently as last year (2019), arrangements and treaties were in their final stages between the two countries to open up the commercial use of CLA as a potential site for USA private firms launches. CLA has the advantage of being the closest of all launch pads to the equator, but it also has nearby competition from a facility in French Guiana, which has been used by several European nations, and the long standing position of Cape Canaveral in Florida, USA.

The Argentina Space agency (CONAE) has the stated mission of providing full launch capabilities for the nation. While involvement by Argentina in the Space community has been active since the 1940s and 50s, and originally as CNIE in 1960, it was not until 1991 that the civilian CONAE was created. To date they have carried out four satellite missions, three of them successful, with the latest in 2018 delivered by a SpaceX Falcon9. The last satellite, and another planned for an upcoming launch, will operate as part of a joint Argentina Italian Cosmo-SkyMed satellite constellation for emergency management communications. The program also has a strong focus on the development of national scientific and technological fields, to include the use of spatial information in educational and productive business applications.

The inclusion of both Argentina and Brazil on the list of nations with or nearly achieving advanced nuclear submarine capabilities and their respective Space programs, paints a good picture of the range of approaches we are likely to see other countries follow. Both AEB and CONAE are currently staffed with roughly 1,000 people and operate on annual budgets of approximately $50 million, each representing even less then the one-half of one percent of the budget that NASA receives in the USA. Monitoring progress in both programs through partnerships, investment of commercial firms, and advancement towards independent full launch capabilities, will provide a road map on how to examine other national Space programs.

Chapter 11 - Space Economy Jobs Earthside

The economic impacts of the Space Economy are not limited to the station because, as previously mentioned, ground crews operating drones and Robonauts will need to be employed. The skills to operate advanced droids, drones, and Robonauts in Space are likely very similar to the skills learned by returning Vets who have experience with forward "technical" capabilities of the modern DoD. We can anticipate that for every drone in Space that there will be between 3-5 jobs created Earthside to enable that drone to operate.

This brings up another ***important point to keep in mind*** with respect to both LEO and the Moon that will not apply the same for the economy on Mars. Most conventional communications in Space are done via radio waves, which travel at the speed of light. Given the speed of light and the distance of Earth based communication, or control elements for droids, the lag to both LEO or the Moon will be no more than your standard VoIP call on Signal. But, it is very important to note that depending on where Mars is in its orbit, the time it will take for communications can range from 3min to 22min. Now we will restrain ourselves from delving into the efficiency of a Lagrangian array being used to speed up communication times but even with that technology, the delay will be significantly greater than "real-time" and be like what you experience when you text your older relatives. It is interesting to think about what longer breaks in communication could mean for future Mars bases and, more long term, what these types of delays would mean for the psychological attachment of Martians to Earth.

Chapter 12 - Space Politics

"The space dream is part of the dream to make China stronger. With the development of space programs, the Chinese people will take bigger strides to explore further into space." -Xi Jinping, President of China

The politics of space seems like a topic that we can get ourselves into trouble with quickly, so let's just dive-in.

First let's look at Space Politics as a natural extension of politics here on Earth. If that just turned your stomach a bit, you can blame it on the zero-Gs. In the same way we have set up rules for how "polite societies" should treat each other in the air and on sea, we also seek to extend rules to how we should all get along in space. Neither of us are Space Lawyers, though in theory couldn't we just create and pass a Bar Exam for that? Maybe for the next book.

So far we have proven that while we continue to use satellites to keep tabs on each other, we can get along on the International Space Station (ISS). We get along so well in fact that since 2011 NASA astronauts have been hitching rides on Roskosmos (RFSA, Russian NASA) rockets since the USA no longer has capabilities to deliver astronauts on our own. (*This was a disgrace. However, on May 30, 2020, NASA and SpaceX launched astronauts Bob & Doug into Space in the first human flight of the SpaceX Dragon capsule. More on that in future books. In the meantime, checkout the Launch America episode on the SpaceChannel.com.*) The ISS is a great example of Earthers all getting along as it has been continuously occupied since 2000 by a revolving crew of up to six, made up of 200+ people from 18 countries. But keep in mind that the ISS is just the latest in a long line of space stations. Prior stations include the Salyut and Almaz series, Skylab, Mir, and Tiangong, most of which were operated for the use of just one country.

Government Space Politics

While it might be nice to envision a singularly focused global future mission in Space that supports and develops the benefits of the Space Economy for everyone, this is just simply not the lay of the land. A wise person once said, "You don't get to make the rules for the sandbox you play in, if you want to do that go pick blades of grass, otherwise figure out the rules, get along with others and don't eat the sand." Politics can be described as the expression of the various voices, financial interests, and fears of a given community of people. Since we all have different voices and like to believe we are motivated differently by money and uniquely affected by fear, it stands to reason that politics will still be alive and well in Space.

Which governments have a voice in Space? Well the answer to that depends on what you are quantifying. Presently, there are only two government space agencies that have full human launch capabilities: Russia and China. Yes the USA cannot be included on this list since, as already mentioned, it has not sent humans to Space without Russian assistance in nearly a decade, although at the time of this book's writing NASA is currently working with SpaceX to transport astronauts to the ISS in the near future. This would make for a very short list if we just looked at astronaut transportation, so another way to frame the conversation is to include nations on a list of achieving full launch capability either human or non-human.

This list would include:

(1) Soviet Space Program (Soviet Union)

(2) NASA (USA),

(3) CNES (France),

(4) UKSA (United Kingdom),

(5) JAXA (Japan),

(6) RFSA (Russia)[12],

---

[12] The Soviet Space Program is listed as is both RFSA for Russia and NSAU for

(7) NSAU (Ukraine),

(8) ESA (22 European Nations),

(9) CNSA (China),

(10)   ISA (Israel),

(11)   ISRO (India),

(12)   ISA (Iran), and

(13)   North Korea

Full launch capabilities, in this context, refers to the ability to put an object into Space via rockets, technologically advanced equipment, and other support systems. A quick read of this list shows 13 nations, some who had capabilities but have since lost them or combined those systems with others. You can also see on this list that one of them, and the first in Space, the Soviet Union, is no longer in existence and several others who famously do not get along are on this list. Again, no matter how you slice it what seems most reasonable to assume is that everyone on this list will not be working together on singular political and government objectives in Space.

As for the USA, it remains the dominant Space power in the world today thanks to the combination of it's manufacturing infrastructure, technical systems, and its use of Space as part of its defense strategy. Having Space as part of the United States' defensive strategy not only integrates and supports the resources dedicated to military missions, but also enhances civilian activity like for humanitarian aid and commercial developments. The dominance, however, of the US in Space power, and by extension politics, is not as large as it once was. The decades NASA spent shifting its mission to focus on Earth observations and the retirement of the shuttles in 2011 has been time and energy spent away from the mission of the cosmos and instead

---

Ukraine. This is done to make clear that while the Soviets first achieved full launch capability Ukraine was not just part of the USSR but a major center for the development of spaceflight technology. It is important therefore to list both Russia as the successor and Ukraine here on this list despite arguments by some that only one entry should be included on this list for the three programs.

spent paying for rides from the Kazakhstan Cosmodrome aboard Russian Soyuz spacecraft.

The United States as the dominant space political power is famous in its role as hegemon for inviting other people to the table. So, in fairness to the many nations with Space ambitions, the list above is also not large or inclusive enough of who has or wants to have a seat at the table. 72 different government Space agencies exist around the globe. These space agencies vary greatly in size and funding and have many different objectives for participation in the Space Economy. Some of the other nations not listed are focused on programs that aim to cooperate and complement current plans by the more active space nations, and others seek to establish alternatives that would be in direct competition with existing players for a piece of the Trillion dollar economic overhead. In this type of environment and with this large a group of political entities, getting everyone to agree on anything seems just as unlikely in Space as it does here on Earth.

Chapter 12a - War as an Extension of Politics.

As often cited by political science teachers, Carol von Clausewitz, famous Prussian general and military philosopher of the early 1800s, said, "War is simply the continuation of politics by other means." Clausewitz's thought of war as a military, political and social phenomenon, also stresses that a continuous aggressor is, more often than not, so focused on the offense they are often found lacking in defensive capabilities, which will inevitably lead to their loss in the long term. Although we are focused on the Space Economy, it is important to both recognize and name the connection to politics, and, by extension, war.

The Space Economy supports the way of life in the United States in peacetime, while at the same time providing capabilities for defense and warfare. It is for these reasons that the power to attack assets in Space, both before and during conflicts on Earth, is becoming more and more important. This new fourth dimension of the battlefield (land, air and sea being the first three) enters the minds of military leaders, strategists and warfighters; other nations will increasingly focus on the development of technology that can take advantage of and capitalize on the new environment. A fifth dimension of modern conflict, and one that is closely tied to Space, is the cyber arena. They connect in several ways, but one of the largest is the ability of military powers to securely acquire, transmit and make actionable, valuable satellite data.

The need to secure both the fourth and fifth dimension of the modern warscape, makes the official establishment of the USA Space Force seem necessary, logical, and timely. Yes, it is true that the last time the Defense Department was reorganized was in 1947 when the Air Force was created out of the Army Air Corps. *Note - We are big fans of the US Coast Guard and have no intention of leaving them out of a discussion of the military branches. For the sake of thoroughness and accuracy, their reorganization from the Department of Transportation to Homeland Security in 2003 was more recent than the creation of the Air Force, but this shift is different from the creation of a new branch of the military under Title 10 of the US Code.*

Much like the creation of the Air Force out of the Army, many of the missions now under the new Space Force emblem are long standing missions of Air Force Space Command that was established in 1982.

The present national security realities and those visible on the horizon include the actions of other major players in Space. Nations like China and Russia but also nations quickly adding to Space capabilities like North Korea and Iran are all part of securing doctrine, policy and normal standards of behavior for how politics will be conducted in Space. The implications of Space on defense policy and politics become clear, and the escalation of indigenous space launch infrastructure from a greater number of nations and actors seems likely in the next several decades. The most obvious of these capabilities is satellites for communication, navigation, tracking, surveillance and spying. The information gathering aspects of a position in Space provides critical advantages to military force strength and currently is a differentiating factor between the USA, which operates nearly triple the number of the next largest other nations or multinationals like China, Russia, ESA and the rest of the world. When troops' movements, stockpiles, and manufacturing capabilities are tracked, we must anticipate it will change behavior. The tracking of activities in the military sphere may keep more policy disagreements to politics, or it might create a greater divide between those nations with and without Space assets and the ability to secure those capabilities from adversaries.

Chapter 12b - Corporate Space Politics

It is also very important to think about the politics of private enterprise in Space. For example, a great case study of this is the three companies currently operating under the NASA Commercial Resupply Services program, SpaceX, Northrop Grumman, and Sierra Nevada Corp, which all have contracted to deliver supplies to the ISS under a $14 Billion program. In the absence of American shuttle capabilities, SpaceX (as previously mentioned) and Boeing have also both been working on private spaceships that can deliver astronauts to the ISS.

"We're rich! The laws of physics don't apply to us!"

-   Penguins of Madagascar 3

Space Politics also involves the efforts of not just private firms but also the Billionaires behind firms like Blue Origin, Virgin Atlantic, and SpaceX. Some, in the not too distant past, have called these companies nothing more than vanity projects while others herald them as acting for the benefit of all mankind. Likely, the answer lies somewhere in between Elon Musk, Jeff Bezos, and Richard Branson have more in common with Zefram Cochrane than they would like to admit. Zefram Cochrane is best known for being the human to create a warp drive in 2063, which led to the first contact between Vulcans and humans in Star Trek. And yes, I am infinitely happier now that I was able to put a reference to Vulcans in a book on Space economics.

Chapter 12c - Moon and Mars Space Politics

Space Politics also gets interesting when we start to think about what laws will be in place for the eventual long-term operations of larger commercial space stations and settlements on the Moon & Mars. We think each of these should be examined in turn with the understanding that they would all be a bit different. First, today's commercial participants in space are reliant on the funding of governments. However, that will likely not be the case as technology improves and the cost of spacecraft and launches continues to come down. Second, as we demonstrated with the satellite industry, as more firms enter the launch, space station, and lunar lander spaces, the growth from 1-to-6,000 is quicker than we can imagine.

Private companies operating under the laws of other nations could quickly deploy space stations, like those being made by Bigelow Aerospace, from the Cosmodrome (Kazakhstan) and set up space laboratories for under $250 Million today with lease rates as low as $15Million a month. Axiom Space also has designs and plans outstanding for private space stations, but less numbers are available. For the point of our discussion we will assume them to be comparable. These laboratories could be crewed or uncrewed, using something like Robonaut, which is an advanced remote-control car with hands, to conduct experiments. This will likely also pick up steam because of the leaps being made in synthetic biology, DNA research, chemistry, and biophysics, all of which will increase demand on space laboratories.

Chapter 12d - Science not Space Politics

As a quick aside, you might be wondering why as costs come down we are so optimistic about the use of commercial spaceports or stations for scientific research. Looking at only the lease option for scientific research, it is important to keep in mind the amount that universities, just in the US, spend on research each year. To put it in perspective with some numbers, the National Science Foundation estimates that US Universities spend $75 Billion[13] on R&D, with the top ten schools: Johns Hopkins, Michigan, UC SanFran, Penn, Duke, Harvard, Stanford, etc. all spending over $1 Billion each. With a one-or-two month lease option at $25 Million from Bigelow, or someone else, what type of research, experimentation, and advances in science might we get from academia? Just looking at R&D spending out of only US Universities would underestimate the size of this market. Many schools from around the world would also be interested and want to participate in this type of advanced research from Toronto, Bucharest, Tokyo, UAE, Beihang, Oslow, Queensland, Nanyang, Delft, Zurich, and more.

Also adding to this Space race in scientific research would be the spending and efforts from companies, particularly those in the medical industry. Biotech, pharma, and healthcare all have potential breakthroughs of new products, markets, and profits from research in Space. Medical industry spending on R&D[14] is more than double what is spent by universities, (near $175 billion). What are the chances that Merck or Johnson & Johnson would also want to conduct research in Space? Novartis is already doing some research on the ISS, and Proctor and Gamble has already earned two patents from their research efforts. We think the chances are pretty good, particularly if smaller firms or new firms out of China or India begin to conduct more research in Space that it becomes an arms race for science. Then as

---

[13] https://www.marketresearchreports.com/blog/2019/04/02/top-10-us-universities-research-spending

[14] https://www.beckershospitalreview.com/finance/healthcare-poised-to-become-largest-r-d-spending-industry-by-2020-study-says.html

breakthroughs like commercialized drugs, and novel medical devices come out of the research, it will push still more firms into space, increasing competition, and thereby innovations that expand humanity.

This demand for R&D in Space, along with the commercial use of satellites that we've already discussed, constitute the chips in the armor of the US government's monopsony. Yes, if you just read that quickly you might have thought we said monopoly, but we didn't. In economics, the two terms are similar but, when used correctly, they identify different dominant forces in a market. The more familiar monopoly is a single seller firm, oligopoly, preventing the function of free market efficiencies. A monopsony, on the other hand, is a single buyer firm that dominates the demand side of the market for goods or services. World government spending on Space is north of $70 Billion[15], but the USA is nearly $41 Billion of that, meaning that well over half of all the money spent in Space makes it out of the gravity known as Washington, DC.

The balance here for the US is how to replace itself with private enterprise as the primary financial supporter in Space but still maintain its position as 100km+ hedgemond. Important to consider is, even with modest spending on R&D in Space above what NASA (and DoD) spend currently, greater financial investments could result in significant advances, technologies, and new businesses. Over 2,000 inventions have come out of NASA and become part of our daily lives, things like: Bowflex gyms, LASIK eye surgery, LED energy efficient lights, OpenStack Cloud computing, Silicon solar power panels, firefighting equipment, and (George's favorite) TEMPUR foam mattresses. When the next LASIK- like medical procedure or Silicon like energy advancement is discovered in Space from private R&D, the role of the US government will shift from one of primary funding of Space to securing, de-risking, and organizing. This seems the likely reason for the Space Force.

---

[15] https://spacenews.com/op-ed-global-government-space-budgets-continues-multiyear-rebound/

Chapter 12e - Space Espionage

"Allow me to introduce you to the airlock chamber. Observe, Mr Bond, your route from this world to the next." -Hugo Drax, Moonraker

Space has always belonged to spies. As far back as ███████████ the ███ and ██████████ were jointly launching the ██████████████ satellites that would take over ████████ photos over the course of ██ years and more than ██ missions. ██████████████████████████

More recently in ████ all the news was abuzz with ████████ aboard the ████████████████████

Author's note - We were going to document a very comprehensive history of espionage in Space and in the Space Industry. However, all that survived the security review was the two paragraphs attached. The rest was ████ pages of redacted text. It's so silly cause we can't even tell you how many pages were redacted. So, if you'd like to discuss the history, reality and potential of Space Espionage from Germany in World War II, the Soviet Union during the Cold War and/or currently with China, ████, North Korea and ████████, email us and we'll work out the details: Official@MilkyWayEconomy.com

Also, it's funny we can mention China and North Korea but not ███ and ██████ when all signs indicate they've as much interest in Space as we do and are worthy adversaries / frenemies / occasional allies depending on how ██████ is threatening the USA.

Chapter 13 - Space Race "3.0"

"From the dawn of time we came; moving silently down through the centuries, living many secret lives, struggling to reach the time of the Gathering; when the few who remain will battle to the last."
-Ramirez, Highlander

One definition for economics is that it's the scientific investigation of how human societies allocate scarce resources. One of the most fundamental of those resources is those that provide us with energy. The allocation of natural resources, such as energy generating minerals like coal, oil, natural gas, and uranium, is critical to an understanding of the development of production. The technology of mechanized industrial activity required greater energy resources and provided larger amounts of output. We have gone through three distinct periods of massive industrialization and are currently going through the fourth such revolution. Understanding the broad characteristics, lessons, and effects of each of these previous and our present industrial revolution, provides you with a greater understanding of the potential for our future in the Space Economy.

Lessons from the First Industrial Revolution (1760- 1840) and Space Coal

If we look back in history at the Industrial Revolution of the mid-eighteenth century, it coincided with the rising use of a particular, pesky, and problematic natural resource for energy, coal. Demand for the black rock grew with the expansion of the steam engine, a critical early industrial machine, which needed high temperature and highly dense energy sources for power. It is easy to make the case that the First Industrial Revolution owed its "spark" to the use of coal, and that the reason that Britain was able to dominate the eighteenth, nineteenth, and the early part of the twentieth century was because of its access to this resource.

Coal, however, was not Britain's first energy resource, and instead it used wood, as did many peoples of other nations in the time period leading up to the First Industrial Revolution. Britain however, had unique geographic realities that complicated the use of wood. As an island, Britain experienced a firewood shortage lasting nearly 150 years, resulting from an intense use of wood for heating and cooking. The shortage put fuel use in competition with industrial use[16], particularly for shipbuilding, and this continued until the 1690s. Wood prices increased nearly 10-fold, created dukes, caused conflicts, and enriched those who could control and harvest the resource from the land. It also contributed to the formation of cultural views, rules, and laws around the use and allocation of land that are still with us today, but maybe more on that later.

Faced with these constraints to production and prices, the British pursued a new resource. Actually, coal was a very old resource but was being newly applied in industrial use. Issues around wood sourcing and finding its place in the energy mix resulted in the explosion of activity around open-pit coal mining. Coal became popular because of its many benefits to include that it was less costly than wood and could be transported more easily. Coal production grew more sophisticated, and mining more widespread, first tripling during the 1700s. This set the stage for the First Industrial Revolution and caused a 25X-increase in coal production during the 1800s.

You might be asking yourself, "What role will coal play in the Space Economy?" None. First of all you get coal, like other fossil fuels, from the compacted prehistoric remains of energy captured by animals and vegetation that accumulated in peat bogs and swamps millions of years ago. Since we don't have any knowledge of animal or plant activity in Space, now or

---

[16] Think of this as the historic equivalent of the modern debate around Ethanol as food versus fuel.

millions of years ago, we can safely say that the off-world portion of the Space Economy will be produced using coal is zero. This does however remind me of one of my kids favorite Space jokes:

Kid: Did you hear about the bones that NASA scientists recently discovered on the Moon?

Me: No! What? When?

Kid: *laughing*

Me: (Eye roll knowing I've been "had") ...

Kid: Yeah, I guess the cow didn't make it!

Okay, back to Space Economy lessons from the industrial revolutions and coal production.

Coal based combustion requires oxygen to produce combustion. Since, like plants and animals, oxygen is not plentiful in Space, this also makes coal a very poor fuel source for Space. However, understanding the role of coal in the first industrial revolution is very important. As it provides us with a framework to construct questions about the importance of energy in the Space Economy. It also shows us how control over a large energy resource allowed the British to dominate up to 25% of the Earth for hundreds of years. When we think about resources that can supply large amounts of energy in Space, we must consider competition for that resource against other uses, such as what we saw with wood for heating, iron working, and shipbuilding. We also need to think about how any resource for energy or industrialization in Space scales, much like what we saw with coal, and if consumption of that resource has any side-effects. Side effects such as global warming, climate change, rising sea levels, increase in pandemics and other side effects of *clean coal* consumption.

It should be noted that the first industry to take advantage of both machinery and more abundant energy was textiles. This success in textile trade led to technology transfer to other areas of the economy of Britain and brought on a period of sustained income and population growth. So, what is the textile industry of the Space Economy, and what industrial and energy markets sit behind it?

Lessons from the Second Industrial Revolution (1860-1910)

The Second Industrial Revolution is largely seen by economists to be a technological revolution versus a resource revolution like the first industrial revolution is regarded. Key among these new technologies was machine tooling, electrification, telegraph and telephone, mass production steel, and railroads. Machine tooling was critical because it allowed for the creation of precision manufactured, standardized, and interchangeable parts. The railroad allowed America to expand westward and connect its coasts with the interior. Electrification, communication advancements, and the railroads allowed for greater connectivity of society.

Electrification. Thomas Edison and Nikola Tesla drove the electrification of cities, and electric lighting grew out of popular demand as light bulbs replaced gas lamps. In industrial applications, steam-powered machines were still being used for several decades but were slowly surpassed by the electric motor and electric powered machines. The amount of additional work a machine could produce with electricity added another force multiplier to the value of labor and the economic output possible for firms. Noteworthy to a student of economics is this rapid technical change was relatively slow at first to take hold. The delay in productivity growth increases has been studied, and it is believed that this delay was caused by slow diffusion of new technologies among manufacturing plants, based on reluctance to switch technologies, combined with the required learning costs after the new technologies had been implemented.

Communication. Communication advancements began with the telegraph and the famous leap forward with the first transcontinental telegram from California to Washington on October 24, 1861. Although important as a feat of electrical engineering, it was also a political act to bring the relatively new state of California deeper into the Union with the rest of the United States. The telegraph line made the infamous Pony Express obsolete, and it officially ceased operations two days later after existing for only about eighteen months. As an aside, did you know that the infamous Pony Express would take 10 days to deliver a message from Sacramento, California to St. Louis, Missouri, a communication now possible in only minutes after the telegraph. The telegraph was also a very important technological and communication advantage for the Union during the Civil War when 15,000 miles of cable were laid. The telegraph, like the Pony Express, had a relatively short life and after the invention of the telephone by Alexander Graham Bell in 1876, it too was displaced. We will see some Pony Express companies in the Space Economy but identifying them early could save you.

Railroads. Mass production of steel and the railroads go together like peanut butter and jelly. Bessemer steel was the first mass produced steel created by using a technique of removing impurities from iron using force air blown through giant egg-like chambers of molten pig iron. It was used extensively by Andrew Carnegie, and he was able to harness the technology to increase output for his businesses and reduce the cost of railroad rails by one-fifth its 1870 cost by the 1890s. If this sounds familiar to the reduction in launch costs previously discussed, it should, and it also provides a framework for analysis of the changes we are seeing. This new technology and the reduction in costs it created laid the groundwork for the crisscrossing of the American landscape with trains. Interesting to note is that the previously mentioned telegraph lines in many areas were constructed alongside railroad lines. This is a great example of technologies seemingly independent but that benefited from each other's growth and development.

Railroads in both Europe and America created a huge change in the time and means by which people and goods crossed distances. Before the invention and widespread adoption of the railroad, people were dependent on horses. Coincidently, it is believed that horses were first domesticated in what is today modern-day Kazakhstan, a major player in the Space Economy because of their Cosmodrome. Waterways were also widely used, but they were available for only some locations as a viable means of moving people and goods. The alternative to horses was one's own feet as a means of transportation like they had been since before the early carts and chariots. Chariots began as an instrument of war, largely believed to be first invented in Mesopotamia, and finding widespread use and adoption by the Egyptians, Greeks, and later Romans, which formed the basis for a technology that spread throughout Earth.

In an era of telecommuting and remote work, we might forget that a large part of a worker's day might have been spent on the distance they had to travel to work. If, however, you are unlucky enough to live in a metropolitan area, you might completely relate to the average commute times north of an hour for so many people. With the invention of the railroad, people had a faster way to get to work, transport goods, and travel for business. Initially, the poor could not afford to use the railroads. However, as it became more widespread, it served to facilitate interstate transportation, improving the availability of goods, and increased productivity for the entire economy.

Although sometimes missed by economic historians and certainly important for us to think about in its applications in the Space Economy is how important this increased ability to transport goods was to the efficient production of supplies. Once again, this is because of economies of scale, a topic we have and will continue to reiterate throughout this text. It cannot be understated how important it is to both recognize the role of this force and its presence throughout previous periods of intense economic development and expansion. It is something we will be seeing again with the Space Economy.

Another thing that railroads brought to the forefront was the need for the creation and widespread use of established official time zones. Never before had people and goods traveled across such great distances at such relatively rapid speeds; hence the coordination of supply chains became a major undertaking. Coordinating the logistics for the orderly loading, unloading and accounting for people and goods moving in between points, also required heightened standards in bookkeeping and the eventual auditing of those records. In the 1880s, railroads in the US began using a standard time system composed of four time zones, Eastern, Central, Mountain and Pacific, which was eventually adopted as law in 1918 with the US Standard Time Act. Interestingly, most large nations have multiple time zones (the USA has nine and Russia has 11, if you ever get asked on Jeopardy) while China only has one. Much like China, Space currently only has one time zone. The ISS (International Space Station) sets its clocks to Zulu time, also referred to as GMT (Greenwich Mean Time), or as UTC (Coordinated Universal Time). Mars also has time zones, and although we are a long way from them being important to economic activity and coordinating travel and trade, we can still thank the early railroaders for Airy Mean Time (AMT). Airy is an homage to George Biddel Airy, who was the scientist who built the original telescope in Greenwich that became the location that defines zero degrees longitude on Earth. It is interesting to consider what time will be used on other bodies in Space, particularly as we look to operate and coordinate activities like asteroid mining. While machines could be set to Zulu time, if human operators or astronauts are involved, maintaining a 24-hour day and night cycle has major implications for both work and our health.

One additional note about the Second Industrial Revolution, is the advent of the internal combustion engine by Nikolaus Otto later "acquired" (we were told not to say stolen) by Gottlieb Daimler and popularized in America by Henry Ford. Since I mostly ride the train in DC and drive an old work truck in Maine, in the same way Samson only uses rideshare services, neither of us are car guys. With that in mind, we don't mean to brush over the automotive industry or its role in the second industrial revolution, it just isn't a subject either of us are terribly versed on and it didn't seem genuine to waste your valuable time on a topic we aren't passionate about.

Chapter 14 - Space Lessons from the 3rd IR (1950-1990)

The Third Industrial Revolution is not so long ago that some readers might have memories of it. It is largely cited as having begun in the 1950s with the creation of digital systems, advanced communication, and the rise of personal computers in the 1980s. This also corresponds to the period discussed early in the first Space Race, early work on satellites, and the focus of our national interest on the stars. The Third Industrial Revolution brought with it transistors, microchips, and automation, which have made possible many of the components of our modern life.

The transistor was invented in 1948 by Bell Labs and is one of the most important inventions of the twentieth century sitting alongside things like nuclear fission (splitting the atom), antibiotics and xerography. The transistor allowed for the radio to amplify weak signals it received and amplify them through speakers. Also, the transistor allowed for machines to switch states of a signal from 0 to 1 and back which is fundamental for all modern digital devices.

It is worth noting here that when someone refers to quantum computing, an often-cited leap in technology for the fourth or maybe fifth industrial revolution, they are referring to a change in this transistor digital design of 0 or 1 to instead a component process capable of performing in a system based on the probability of an object's state. To simplify this with a familiar example, think of a baseball player who with each pitch could receive a (0) strike or a (1) ball thrown across the plate. This calling of the pitch is the function of a transistor - our home plate umpire. By comparison, with super positioning and entanglement a quantum computing system by contrast is predicting all the play action after our batter swings at the ball using qubits, hence far more than a two-choice problem. The ball could do any number of things including: plant in the catcher's glove, go rolling down the third base line, pop-fly to deep center, homerun, hit the pitcher, or land shallow behind the first base, and in all these states of the ball the players would also have a variety of actions. Taken together, this creates a probability density function that economists are familiar with from

84

econometrics, but in this application represents the portion of time the quantum mechanical system spends in various locations representing each potential future state.

Transistors went through a major upgrade when they went from the original germanium to the now standard silicon-based material. This was done because germanium has a tendency to breakdown at high temperatures, and the machinery and devices transistors were placed in continued to produce greater temperatures with increased sophistication.

The transistor led to the microchip (1959) by Texas Instruments, which is manufactured from a semiconducting material much like the transistor. The difference in the two technologies is that the microchip or microprocessor or RAM chip is a collection of transistors in a single component that form a circuit. This allowed for more complicated logic functions and formed the important "guts" of modern computers. In addition to the collection of transistors, a microchip also often includes resistors and capacitors that are together etched onto a single tiny component. Interesting to note, since microchips are created using chemicals, gases and light, all of which can be varied and controlled in unique ways in a Space laboratory environment, they also form the basis for a entire new industry of potential manufacturing of advanced microchips in Space for application both in LEO but also back on Earth.

Automation was made famous with Henry Ford's assembly line. In the Third Industrial Revolution the application of transistor and microprocessor technology allowed for partial automation using new memory programmable controls. Memory programmable controls can be thought of as a system of transistors that provide automation to the processes being controlled on the control panel of a ship. Automation allowed for advancements in energy systems like those on the steam boilers of ships and production processes. From the panel controls of ships, to factories, to assembly lines, the processing power of transistors, and later computers, allowed more and more to occur without or with only limited human assistance.

The Internet provided both greater communication and access to information for business management and communities. Although not often cited, the internet provided the spark for firms to realign production and capabilities from mass production to lean manufacturing. New systems like JIT (just-in-time) and TQM (total quality management) began changing economic systems and thinking in ways not seen before. With this new ability of management and firms with the computers and the internet to spread supply chains out into new regions (capturing cost advantages in production from cheap labor and lack environmental standards), it allowed for the monitoring of information around the quality of components in these more complex networks. JIT started with Toyota in the 1970s and is based around a system of manufacturing where little to nothing is kept in inventory and all parts arrive at a plant just in time for installation in the final product. TQM, a complement to many JIT businesses, focuses on adhering to internal standards and process guidelines to reduce errors. TQM also ensures that all parts of production are held accountable for overall quality, and improvements are constantly examined and applied to streamline production or delivery of services.

Coronavirus Update

Coronavirus Update: Yes, most of this was written before the Coronavirus, and we will have to dedicate some time to providing new analysis (where appropriate) for systems, economic models, and societal norms impacted, but it is impossible to take edits on this section without adding in how JIT and TQM have been shown to include epic failures of these systems in the face of a global pandemic. Just-in-time has shown itself to not work well when the organization, time, and effort required to switch production is so sufficiently complicated that delivery of life saving devices is delayed. TQM, as applied by many firms, also shows that the constant streamlining of complex supply chains spread across multiple continents and countries also performs very poorly during a crisis. N95 masks, PPE, and testing reagents have all been shown to have limited stockpiles and come from a limited number of suppliers who lack the ability to scale quickly enough to ease public fears. All of which is further complicated by the need to often structure multinational coordination of component chemicals, parts and materials not easily accessible near the manufacturing centers. In short, though we are heading to Space as a nation, we should probably bring PPE and critical infrastructure component manufacturing back to America

Chapter 15 - GPS and GNSS

Global Navigation Satellite Systems are always difficult to categorize as either part of the Third or Fourth Industrial Revolution. Yet, they deserve inclusion on one of the two lists for the huge advancement in technology, geolocation, and time it provides using satellites. The reason it is difficult to place it is because the technology and widespread use of the first of these systems, called GPS (Global Positioning System) originally came out of the US Department of Defense (DoD) as the NAVSTAR radio navigational system, creating a new form of communication in the 1970s. GPS does not require the user to have access to telephone or internet.

Since the original NAVSTAR GPS system was rolled out, it has gone through many changes to include, most importantly, the per missioning of commercial use. This is similar to the way that scientific research from universities and businesses can apply to participate in investigations on the International Space Station (ISS). GPS service and its over 30 satellites are still permissioned by the government of the United States. Because of this permission and the implications that has for other nations dependent on it, a few have copied the technology and launched similar systems. One very public example of this was when the US denied service to India during the Kargil War with Pakistan in 1999.

The incident pushed India to develop its own Space navigation system of GNSS. The IRNSS-NAVIC was launched between 2013 and 2018 and has a primary focus of coverage for India, plus an area extending up to 1,500 km around its borders. The program is made up of 8 satellites, which have half their satellites in geostationary orbit and half in geosynchronous orbits to create the necessary two orbital planes for GNSS to be most effective. Prior to the Indian program, the Russian Global Navigation System had been also operating at the same time as the US NAVSTAR during the Cold War and is also the second largest with 24 satellites. The Russian satellite navigational system called GLONASS is now available for commercial use in combination with US NAVSTAR, and are commonly used together in smart watches, iPhones, and cars. The combination of services is said to improve accuracy and coverage, but also allows GPS users the GLONASS quick satellite lock when you first start your devices.

The other three major GNSS operators are China with BeiDou, the European Union with Galileo, and Japan with QZSS. Much like the Indian IRNSS-NAVIC GNSS, the Galileo system by the European Union was launched as a way to provide an option to subvert the dependency of Europe on using either the US or Russian systems. It has made consistent launches since 2005 and went operational back in 2016, currently operating almost 30 satellites. The Galileo system is unique in several ways, one of which being redundancy in the form of spare satellites already in orbit, and ready for repositioning should a problem arise with another satellite in the aray. Galileo is also the only system that is completely under civilian control and not operated by the military. Being operated in dual frequency by default offers Pseudo Random Noise (PRN) accuracy that is down to 20cm, a major improvement over the 3-meter reliability of GPS. Unique to the JAXA operated QZSS (Quas-Zenith Satellite System) is that Japan operates in partnership with the US GPS NAVSTAR service to provide enhanced coverage for the Asia and Oceania regions. Japan has also announced plans to, in addition to the QZSS system, launch a separate independent system over the next decade. Finally, the BeiDou system, which is not yet complete but has been a decade long project, is expected to be completed by summer 2020. The Chinese version of GPS like NAVSTAR and GLONASS is meant to operate as a worldwide coverage network and has already received wide adoption in other parts of Asia, the Middle East and Africa.

Chapter 16 - The Fourth IR is happening Today

Since we are currently in the mist of the Fourth Industrial Revolution this can only be based half on what can be observed, and half based on what we can reasonably predict. Throughout our discussion so far we have talked about the types of forces that have come out of industrial revolutions that have had general purpose benefits from these technologies and how along the way the formation of interdependencies in technological systems takes place.

Fourth Industrial Revolution Technologies, or 4IR tech as it is referred to in popular media, is being marked by our advancements in AI, blockchain, cloud computing, genetics, 3D-printing, big data, energy, and more. Some of these advancements are observable in economic systems and businesses now. The real benefits and breakthroughs, as outlined in the previous industrial revolutions, will come from the convergence of these new technologies with existing systems and the way that they interact and compete with the legacy businesses we are familiar with. The theme of the Fourth Industrial Revolution has been that convergence is happening faster or as some have called it "faster miracles". Discovery in scientific research when combined with cross disciplinary projects, learning and thinking leads to innovation at an exponential rate that is difficult for many to keep up with or conceptually appreciate the implications of. It is difficult to predict the ways all of these technologies can interact and build on each other to form our future but understanding that they are is important.

"The most important thing to do in artificial intelligence is just dive in!"

- General Jack Shanahan United States Air Force

Chapter 17 - 4IR Artificial Intelligence

Artificial intelligence is a broad term that includes things: like machine learning, natural language processing, deep learning, and neural networks, which are fundamentally all part of a category of computer software that does something "smart". The science and engineering of making machines smart is only just getting started, but already we see programs capable of visual categorizing, speech recognition, translation, and decision making. In its simplest form, AI can be thought of as a large collection of if-then statements. AI can also include things like complicated statistical models and recognition of symbolic relationships across inputs. In some of these algorithms, the programs run are able to adapt with the presentation of new and greater information, producing novel outputs without a reliance on human experts.

These novel outputs are often referred to as "learning" by the artificial intelligence program. What is happening is, the algorithms inside the program are seeking to optimize along an output dimension based on the data available to the system. This output function seeks to minimize loss or errors in the course of achieving its objective. These errors are often determined based on ground-truth or training data labeled pertaining to the output. One type of program that does this is a neural network, which seeks to adjust the algorithm with each new iteration to reduce the errors and achieve the objective function. Deep or reinforcement learning is an extension of neural networks where layers of neural networks enable the program to learn features of the data in feature hierarchies, with each subsequent layer applying more mathematical operations and adding to the computational complexity.

Chapter 18 - 4IR Cloud Computing

Cloud computing has been all the rage in IT for the past several years and it does not look to be a trend that will be ending anytime soon. The advantages of cloud computing come from a variety of factors since it enables flexibility, cost savings, connectivity, mobility. Arguably, one of the most important features that aids in its popularity is how it provides rocket fuel for Software as a Service (SaaS) for firms. SaaS allows firms to concentrate on their business and rely on vendors for providing business applications that update versions without the firm having to do anything. This immediate upgrade of software can make new features available quickly, and that can keep workers more productive and the firm's information more secure. The flip side of this advantage is that once a firm is locked in with a vendor, they no longer own the hardware that runs their applications or data storage.

Since not all data is equally as valuable or interacts with an enterprise in the same way, normally firms will have a hybrid and multi-cloud approach for data governance based on the needs like data retrieval. As the amount of data increases and the rate is also increasing, storage powered by the cloud becomes a frequent choice. An example of this large amount of data can be seen with autonomous cars that are estimated to generate and consume between 5-10TB of data for one hour of driving. Since sending this volume of data to a public cloud for processing would not be easily accomplished, a related system called edge computing is also viewed as a technological solution. Depending on latency needs for applications, it is easy to envision the use of satellites for micro-data centers and micro-clouds where the data is created and transformed and then quickly transmitted back to Earth. This will be important for the greater use of virtual assistants, augmented and virtual reality (AR/VR), artificial intelligence or "smart" devices, industrial automation, predictive maintenance and diagnostics, bioinformatic collection, and IoT devices that will have certain functions and processes that require processors for algorithms that would contribute to large battery drains if not handled away from the device itself.

Chapter 19 - 4IR Genetics and Healthcare

The speed that we have gone from Maurice, Franklin, Watson and Crick exploring crystallography and figuring out the structure of DNA to the doorstep of synthetic biology has been in less than the average human lifetime, and it is just getting started. The molecule forms the foundation for heredity. The laws of Mendelian inheritance that form the basis of our understanding of heredity comes from the work 100 years earlier by Abbot Gregor Mendel, who is famous for his early experimentation with pea plant characteristics. *(Peas are important in the Space Economy, but we will save that more for our discussion of how everyone living and working in future space stations and the Moon is Vegan.)* All proteins constructed in the body, including those for disease, come from patterns imprinted in DNA. The insights provided by understanding the double helix of two chains of alternating sugar and phosphate groups held together with hydrogen bonds and the bases—adenine (A) with thymine (T), and guanine (G) with cytosine (C) have formed the basis for biotechnology.

Clustered Regularly Interspaced Short Palindromic Repeats (CRISPR) is a type of DNA sequence found in the genomes of bacteria like the one that gives you strep throat. This bacteria that infects nearly a billion people a year around the world uses a special protein that Jennifer Doudna and Emmanuelle Charpentier were able use as the basis of a groundbreaking system allowing for the cutting of DNA and preparing it for combination with new DNA. This revolutionary gene-editing technology holds the promise (and danger) to enable people to control their own genes and those of other things living around them.

Some of the applications include controlling gene expression, often described as the reprogramming of cells, which is sure to unlock new advances in medicine. The applications of synthetic biology to invent new biological systems and reimagine existing ones can expand the functions of mammalian cells. This could be used to invent therapies that enable the

93

body's own cells to seek out cancer tumors and treat them with the body's own immune system. There are also applications for farming to help grow food cheaper, with less pesticide, and with enhanced nutritional characteristics or genetically modified to perform better in Zero-G.

Genetics is the first example of the major changes happening in the larger healthcare industry, but plenty of other advancements are also taking place. One of the bigger ones is the move to electronic medical records that create consolidated, secure, and complete medical histories. As we approach a doctor shortage in the USA and around the World in the 2030s, the importance of medical professionals being able to easily, and efficiently deliver— and likely with the help of AI— healthcare through things like tele-medicine or remote medicine will become even more important. Also, as the use of genetics and synthetic biology continue to push the science of pharmaceuticals, customized medicine becomes a reality.

The future of medicine is having complete medical records and information in a machine-readable format that can help optimize the formulation, and delivery of a drug therapy for all Humanity. Currently, the majority of drug treatments work best for someone who is of primarily Northern European descent, male, over 115kg, with O negative blood and an underactive MSTN gene. This is the case because clinical trials are conducted on homogenous groups of males, of Northern European descent. As we head into the future of genetic research and drug discovery in Space, we implore the research community to do so with a wider, more inclusive look at including women, Black men, Black women and other Women and Minority groups of Color in clinical trials and medical research.

New data and the empowerment to use that data in healthcare could also change current healthcare industry economics. One of the possibilities is the creation of prosumers, which are people who both consume and are involved in the design, manufacture, or development of a product. In the case of the production of health, it involves the use of digital platforms likely accessible from mobile phones that can offer highly customized healthcare services to individuals, and feedback on diet, activity, and lifestyle. Imagine a Fitbit that knows not only just how many steps you have taken, but also your complete blood count, DNA, and full medical history combined with an advanced Justine[17] style virtual assistant.

---

[17]Justine, in addition to being one of my favorite names, is the virtual assistant in the movie 'Why Him?' that was created by an immature genius tech millionaire and voiced by Kaley Cuoco from "The Big Bang Theory" fame.

Chapter 20 – 5th IR = SPACE

Framing Space Race 3.0 as part of the Fifth Industrial Revolution and putting it in context with the other four major economic, technologic, and social shifts, allows us to better appreciate the significance of what is happening today. Tapping into the resources of Space will have much the same economic significance for the nations and companies that lead as did coal for Britain 250 some odd years ago. Although the ability to have satellites mounted with solar panels beaming concentrated solar energy back to the Earth is a possibility, the resources we seek in space are not energy in the same way that coal was for the British. Instead in Space it will be data, scientific discovery, and expansion of territory.

Data is the new oil. Data is gold.

Several CEOs have made public statements saying they believe that their warehouse of customer data is potentially more valuable than their entire current business enterprise. Data in Space is not just a resource we will collect looking out into the Cosmos, it is a resource we are already collecting as we look down onto and into ourselves.

We collect this data using satellites, about 2,200, as of January 2020. We have come a long way since Sputnik and to help better understand this, I want you to think about Zack Morris from 'Saved by the Bell' (the first non-cartoon show I watched with regularity) and the Pentagon's recently announced plans. The technology in your pocket, hand, or jacket reading this book to you over your earbuds shares much in common with what's in satellites. So much so that back in 2014 NASA launched several "Dove" nanosatellites using consumer-grade smartphones modified only by a small box to help charge, navigate, and relay data. That technology used to be in devices the size of buildings. Over just a few short decades it shrunk to the size of a bus, then a microwave size Zack Morris cell phone, and now your Samsung Note 10. Along the way, the technology didn't just get smaller, it got better and cheaper. This three-part benefit has come about partially due to the economies of scale of 5-billion cell phones being made and in-use today.

The Pentagon has said it will be building and launching a new satellite each week over the next several years. The more launches the better the tech gets for future spacecrafts. The more we build the better we get at it. The greater the number of firms, people, and resources directed towards this endeavor, the faster the knowledge is spread into other areas of the economy. The incredible future growth in satellites is likely to be a stand-alone trillion-dollar industry. This further advances eventual spaceports, Moon, and Mars missions. Convergence of these forces is where the exponential growth comes from.

Important to remember is that raw data is not in and of itself power. Raw data is the equivalent of jumbled letters of the alphabet in wood. Information, however, is when Gutenberg puts the alphabet onto printing metal blocks and books go from the monasteries of Europe to the masses. These mountains of raw data from satellites will be transformed into "books" of information about every aspect of human life here on Earth. The rise of mass printing books, namely the Bible, gave way to a demand for learning, the creation of Universities, and the sparks of literacy over five hundred years ago. What will the rise of this mountain of raw data lead us to demand, create and make common place?

Data from satellites alone is not the only resource, technology, or economic incentive for the New Space Race. The, not just possible but likely, scientific discoveries awaiting us in Space are also a major driver of this new chapter.

Chapter 21 - New Energy

If data is the new oil and oil is gold, what is the new energy? The answer is not straightforward and while the likely option for electric power in Space seems to be a combination of nuclear and solar it is still far too early to tell what other systems or resources may be developed, e.g.: dark matter, ion drives, solar winds. Some young engineer and budding inventor is likely in her first year of college right now with an idea for a new system for energy that will be just what is needed to fuel the Fifth Industrial Revolution. This source of fuel may even help improve launches and could the new breakthroughs in energy could even go so far as to translate into a new way of living on Earth. It is important to stay open to not just advances in nuclear and solar but also a whole host of potential new energy resources we cannot yet conceive.

Scientific Discovery for Profit

NASA spends a relatively small amount on scientific research, analysis and discovery in Space. To be clear this is separate from what is spent on technology to get off Earth, satellites to look at Earth, telescopes, heliophysics and deep space. Out of the most recent budget, approximately 45% was dedicated to human space flight and a bit less than half of that is funding for continuing funding of the International Space Station (ISS). This budget is made up of a long list of items but a few of them worth noting include paying about $86 million for each seat aboard Russia's three-person Soyuz spacecraft for trips to the International Space Station (ISS), and only $350 million for ISS research.

ISS research representing only a bit over 1.50% of NASA's budget has taken place at a relatively similar rate over the last 17 years, as astronauts have worked and lived continuously onboard. The ISS has advanced scientific research and knowledge, while at the same time helping to develop new technologies that benefit from its special location. To date, the unique microgravity laboratory has been part of over 2,500 research investigations and experiments, with 3,400+ investigators participating and more than 1,600 R&D results published in scientific journals and magazines. These projects include studies from the fields of remote sensing, drug therapies, monitoring weather, physical sciences, life sciences, improving equipment for first responders, producing unique fiber-optics (ZBLAN) and technology.

This research has included specific research into exercise, nutrition and drug use for the treatment of osteoporosis, a condition affecting millions. Other research has focused on the DNA of microorganisms capable of surviving interplanetary spaceflight. Medical research has also been devoted to the study of gene-folding. An important area of pharmaceutical development is understanding the shape of protein molecules and crystallography, which, because it is inhibited by gravity, is able to be experimented with in the absence of convection and the settling out of denser particles allowing the crystals in microgravity to be much larger and easier to analyze, facilitating the study of the microstructures and interaction for therapies in muscular dystrophy and cancer. The physics of fire and combustion in microgravity have also been studied because fuel forms into tiny droplets under microgravity and when ignited are incredibly efficient, laying the foundations for advancements in combustion and reducing carbon fuel consumption on Earth.

This research portfolio represents a small part of NASA's budget, but beyond that an infinitesimal part of the overall money spent on research and development. As commercial Space provides options for space stations that can be built for a single company or leased out by several, the growing community of researchers who can put their scientific dreams beyond the limits of gravity will increase exponentially. Those forging ahead in this leadership in commercial space for the purposes of research will discover groundbreaking science not possible on Earth. The first use of specialty nanofluids developed in Space, used in the delivery of a groundbreaking medicine or a commercial application of cold flames, will change everything.

This is all without trying to push the bounds of imagination too much and entertaining the possibility of discovery with the Cold Atom Laboratory (CAL) which produces clouds of ultracold atoms known as Bose-Einstein condensates (BEC), the study of which could advance our understanding of quantum physics and the wavelike nature of matter. So put simply, a discovery in any one of these industries stemming from research in Space could launch an incredible escalation of demand for access to research capabilities off Earth.

Chapter 22 - Far and Away the Colonization[18] of Space

Lastly, and maybe the hardest to understand, is the economic benefits from sheer expansion of territory. Consider the value of a large assembly room floor or the size of a home in Ohio or Maine versus NYC or DC. It is perhaps difficult for us to understand because we did not grow up in a century of exploration, colonization, or conquest. Land is, of course, always necessary for expansion, but so is bread. In classical economics, land is placed as one of the three factors of production, alongside labour and capital. Land is typically understood to take on two values (1) for the services and (2) the stock of land. A good example of the two parts of this value for land is in the movie "Far and Away" where Joseph (Tom Cruise) is willing to risk his life, on multiple occasions, for access to the limited stock of land being given away freely by the US Government[19] in Oklahoma circa 1890s. The land he is after would be better if it also had access to water, thereby enhancing its potential to render service for his economic pursuits, but that is a separate concern after simply occupying his own land. So, will land in Space win you the heart of Nicole Kidman, well we don't know the answer to that. But, what we do know is that in a similar way to "Far and Away" a land race is already underway in Space. The current most valuable land is the orbital pathways of LEO followed by MEO (Medium Earth Orbit), and GEO (Geosynchronous Equatorial Orbit). The Iridium Communications Network will consist of 66 satellites when complete and Starlink is slated for

---

[18] Author's Note - We do not take lightly the concept of colonizing space. The wounds of colonization remain fresh even today in the United States America, throughout the Americas, Africa, the Middle East, India and globally. In Book II of the Milky Way Series, *Race in Space - Racial Equity & Justice in the Space Economy* our resident anthropologist Samson Williams tackles the concept of the colonization of Space, institutional racism and what these factors mean for permanent Human settlements in Space.

[19] This "free" land was of course not free. Rather it was stolen thru colonization from the Cherokee, Chickasaw, Choctaw and Seminole and Muscogee Nation. In July 2020, the Supreme Court of the United States ruled that nearly 50% of eastern Oklahoma falls within an Indian reservation. How this will affect Oklahoma as a state is a fast-developing story.

12,000. Who gets the first claim to this "land" in Space? Based on our experience in Oklahoma, it would appear to be whoever grabs the flag first.

The three rules in real estate will be the same for Space as they are on Earth: location, location, and location.

Chapter 23 - Space Force

"Ambition is exhilarating but without a framework it can end up being like a dog chasingits tail, fun to watch but pointless all the same." - Maine Grandfather Wisdom

Policies of the government, investments of businesses, and support of academics, technologists, and a labor force will allow for economic success in Space. Infrastructure is a huge part of the puzzle, followed closely by education and financial capital.

The types of infrastructure needed are broken down between Earthbound and Space. Gravity is a powerful "frenemy", which is the major reason for the split when discussing infrastructure. Massive heavy industry taking place in Space to support the building of satellites, Spaceports, and Spacecraft is required for the harvesting of Space riches. In addition, supporting a community in Space will require both water and special agricultural techniques to make sure the population in Space is fed without being 100% dependent on costly shipments, and squandering precious room on rockets.

UNITED STATES SPACE FORCE
MMXIX

Another part of this required infrastructure is the Space Force. If you are worried about Space Politics, Space Espionage, Space Trash, or Conflict affecting your multi-million dollar space investment; you would likely feel much better if some of those concerns had been de-risked by the US government. This is not unlike how we de-risk the Middle East for Oil companies. Incentives must be aligned in Space to reward investment, effort, and ingenuity.

To Boldly Go Where No One Has Gone Before, Well Almost

The work of formally creating the Space Force as an independent branch of the US military can be traced back to the reestablishing of the National Space Council in June of 2017. The National Space Council is the second, or third depending on how you count it, incarnation of the National Aeronautics and Space Council that was established in 1958, helping to set up NASA and operating through the space race until it was disbanded in 1973. It was then reconstituted under President George H.W. Bush, but was subsequently abolished again in November of 1993 when then president Bill Clinton moved many of its functions to the National Science and Technology Council. The period from then until the announcement in June of 2010 by then president Barack Obama of the National Space Policy is viewed by many as a "time when the US gave up ground in Space" to other nations as efforts from NASA and DoD were redirected towards inward looking Earth observations and not outward looking science, technology, and exploration.

The Obama National Space Policy changed all that by providing first of its kind guidance for commercial, civil, and national security space sectors, and the promotion of US business interests in the Space Economy. The principles of the policy stated that the US is committed to encouraging and facilitating the growth of the US commercial Space sector, its global competitiveness, and advancing US leadership in the generation of new markets, and innovation-driven entrepreneurship. It was also briefly entertained by President Barack Obama that the National Space Council would be reestablished as a way to bridge the gap between civil and military space agencies but that was never actualized.

Then on June 18th, 2018 President Donald Trump announced the formation of a Space Force separate from the Air Force and framed US space exploration as both a matter of national identity and a matter of national security. From the time of the announcement to the time of this writing, many questions remain, including how the Space Force will operate given the Outer Space Treaty. The United Nations approved agreement set up 53 years ago is the guiding star of international Space law, which to-date has over 100 nations as parties to the document. The treaty is a list of things that nations can and can not do in Space, that helps provide a safe use of Space by all nations. It is a principle-based document, not a set of governing rules, which is a framework stemming from the state of relative infancy space technology was in at the time and the need to be flexible enough to accommodate future situations.

One of the topics we have previously discussed comes up here. The "Far and Away Space Colonization" effect is that in the Outer Space Treaty, such behavior is specifically prohibited, meaning, no country can claim the Moon or an asteroid for itself. Not mentioned in the treaty, however, is what role big business might have to play. Given the state of the world and economies in 1967, it is fair to say many people alive and in positions of power would recall or have studied the age of big business starting in the period after the Civil War and running through the 1920s. Being aware of the growth, motivations, and power (rivaling that of many nations) that a big business might possess and not expressly prohibiting them from claiming ownership of the Moon, asteroids, or other Space assets like the treaty did for nations has led man to interpret this to be an opportunity for commercial Space firms. This was solidified still further in the US by the 2015 Commercial Space Launch Competitiveness Act. This move was followed by similar policy moves by Luxembourg in 2017, and UAE in 2019.

It is important to point out that, also in 2015, both Russia and China made major moves to realign policy and military assets in Space. China created the PLA Strategic Support Force, which combined operational abilities and control over cyber, electronic networks, and space warfare. In a similar move, Russia combined many of the same systems and operations now under the US Space Force into what they have labeled the Russian Aerospace Forces. As of today, cyber is not under the control of the US Space Force, an important distinction between the changes in the military structure in China and that of the US and Russia. Since the next conflict will likely involve both the cyber and space plane, the coordination of these activities could provide major advantages to nations that are able to organize them. One such example would be the hacking of satellites to turn off the "eyes" over a battlefield or create momentary chaos.

The Outer Space Treaty also lays out rules for space, prohibiting overt military activities like: weapons testing, military bases, war games, and the placement of nuclear weapons into orbit on the Moon or any other celestial body. Impossible for the drafters of the document to know over fifty years ago, is the prolific use of satellites for support of many of these activities on Earth. On December 20th, 2019, Space Force was established officially as an independent service, which was around the same time as this book was first being conceptualized by the authors.

The Air Force, as the last independent service to be established, was originally part of the Army. The Army presented with the invention of the Wright Brothers flown at Kitty Hawk in 1903 and the powder keg of World War I it was only a bit over 10 years later that by 1914 we not only had airplanes in regular military service but also the first recorded dog fight. The use of airpower became critical in World War II, and in every major conflict since, it has been this new dimension of warfare that has provided the US with an advantage. The most obvious example of this is with Operation Desert Shield. In 1991 Saddam Hussein's Iraqi forces were defeated and beaten back from the positions they had taken occupying their neighbor Kuwait over the course of a few nights. The images of the night bombings on American television screens is still a distinct cultural memory for many. It is important to point out that, at the time of the war, Iraq's army was considered the 4th largest and among the strongest in the world. This use of one-sided dimensional dominance could be seen again in Space. If we go even farther back in our history books, we can see it with both sea and land power, but in the meantime the majority of activities that don't escalate to the level of open conflict occur via asymmetric and nonconventional means, but explaining cyber and the economy as dimensions of warfare is a token of a different color.

It took time to get from Snoopy-esq aerial combat to the types of aero-acrobatics people are familiar with from movies like Top Gun in 1986. The timeline for flight stretches in both directions if we just take a slightly broader perspective. Because, and in fairness to the Wright Brothers, many gliding machines (omitting Leonardo da Vinci's 1485 ornithopter) began a hundred years early, and starting with George Cayley onward into a large collection of machines and attempts in the 1850s, laid the foundation for the scientific exploration of the forces of weight, drag, lift and thrust. Maybe the work of the last seventy years has been more similar to gliding than flying and what we today call "launch" will be remembered as such by the history books with "spaceflight" as a separate category of travel. Given the importance of Space to modern civilizations, reliance on satellites for communication, banking (ATMs), GPS, entertainment, and defense combined with the examples from history of the outcomes stemming from open conflict when faced with an adversary with dimensional dominance, it is no wonder the US Space Force was created.

Chapter 24 - Space Force and 22nd Century Warfare

News reports about the Pentagon in early 2020 included discussion of proposed legislation for Congress bringing personnel from the Army, Navy, and Marines into the newly inaugurated Space Force. The idea is that the new branch of the military, the first such branch created since the Air Force, will be an extension of the existing missions, but also able to grow out of the work that has come before it within the DoD (Department of Defense) to create a new service focused on "22nd century warfare" as described by Air Force Maj. General John Shaw.

That history includes the work of the Fourteenth Air Force and Air Force Space Command (AFSPC) that was first established back in 1982 with headquarters at Peterson Air Force Base, Colorado, USA. The focus of AFSPC has been to provide the military with focused capabilities, from a global perspective, to the joint warfighting team. Their mission is focused on providing resilient, defendable, and affordable space capabilities for the Air Force, the Joint Force and the Nation. Much like the Army's Mad Scientist Laboratory program, both initiatives are focused on innovation, collaboration and accelerating combat readiness, technology development, and organizing for warfighting success in the battlefields of the future.

It is important to note that prior to AFSPC, The Space and Missile Systems Center (SMC), a subordinate unit created in 1954, was the center of technical excellence for developing, acquiring, fielding and sustaining military space systems. From the late 1950s through the 1960s, the SMC helped develop Atlas, Titan, Thor, and Minuteman missile systems. SMC is also in-charge of on-orbit check-out, testing, sustainment and maintenance of GPS, military satellite constellations and other DoD Space systems.

The rapid shift in technology, that will be both the adversary and ally of future nations in conflict, includes the need to not just develop Space assets but also artificial intelligence, secure communication, advanced satellites, automated drones, and next generation cyber defensive capabilities. With respect to the development of Space assets, the first step will be to identify, adapt, and deploy warfighting operational capabilities currently deployed in Earth settings that have the capability to pivot to Space. Given the unique nature of the environment of Space, it is likely that missions, lessons, and technologies will be pulled from all the other services.

Much of the doctrine in Space has lessons to build on the domain experience from undersea warfare, i.e., submarines. (It should be noted that although it is an active point of contention to many in the Twitterverse, the current structure of Space Force follows that of the Air Force, and not the rank or alignment structure of the Navy which is more typical in Sci-Fi depictions such as the United Nations Navy and Marine Corps in the Expanse.) The parallel most often cited for submarines has to do with the reliance on communication, coordination, and visualization for mission accomplishment; versus attribution like what is possible with both land and air based battlespaces. Put simply, if you drop a missile on a tank or take a beach you can rely on attribution from both warfighter accounts on the ground, in the air, and enhanced by satellite location and images, but when two submarines are engaged, think Hunt for Red October, you are relying on the visualization of data.

While the primary mission for the current moment in time is securing the space, capabilities provided by satellite assets; as more nations expand their launch technology the chance for conflict grows. All battle plans, like economic models, go out the window when the first bullets fly and reality hits, but it is the important role of learning, planning, and analysis that comes out of those efforts that creates the necessary state of preparedness.

The role of government is to de-risk. De-risking activity is job 1, 2 and 3 of Space Force. For the Space Force, and DoD in general, the role is to de-risk conflict, but more broadly, governments function as a mechanism to de-risk: crime, sickness, fire, potholes, and medicine (in some places).

With government involvement at its current concentrations in the Space Economy, it creates economic models that are not well suited for dealing with scenarios involving firms as price makers, partial information, non-mobile labor, and high costs of market failures. Each of these issues has a solution available to firms participating in a free-market economy that can be observed and brought over to Space.

Chapter 25 - De-Risking Off World Ventures & Space Insurance

One of the solutions to the high costs of failure risk that exist in free markets, both with and without government participation, is insurance. Yes, the "I" word. The insurance business in general is normally regarded as the quiet middle child of the financial sector. It is a line of business focused on risk which is, even after the Global Financial Crisis in 2008 and other Black Swan events, often placed in the afterthoughts of a firm's financial positioning. This problem is also common with those operations found within the CRO (Chief Risk Officers) authority, but this is a mistake. However, when it comes to the Space Economy and in particular launch, insurance is always part of the conversation. The ability to financially cover failure is an important part of allowing for the successful commercialization of Space. When Space was just the playground of nations, and governments were self-insured by taxpayers for liabilities around launch and orbital systems. Back then the need for liability coverage did not exist but now with the growing private Space sector it is a crucial piece of the economy.

At its core, insurance is the exchange of premium, by a group of entities exposed to risk, that is paid to an entity outside of that risk, and able to pay claims in the event of losses. (*While we are tempted to use a health insurance example, with the rate of potential hospital bankruptcies in the near future due to Covid19 it seems better to use an example around car insurance.*) Car insurance is a good example of this structure for the industry. There are almost 300 million automobiles registered to be on the road in the USA, and about 85% of them are insured. This creates a very large pool of drivers to pay premiums in the event that a few of them each year hit each other. The basic scenario is that a driver pays premiums to protect against the financial risk of an accident each month (or twice a year for a discount with the gecko) and only files a claim once every twenty years. So while 6,500+ accidents a day result in injury, disability or death, that number is spread across a very large pool of drivers and vehicles each paying $150 or so dollars per month.

The insurance numbers work out very differently for the Space industry as compared to cars. To begin, everyone is treated like a teenage driver, so premiums are significantly higher. Space insurance policies often pay out due to things like: rocket failure, in-orbit collisions, and damage to satellites in transport prior to launch. Next, for the last ten years there have been only between 70 and 111 launches per year, already the pool of potential customers for launch insurance is considerably smaller. Now, launch is not the only category of Space insurance, because it also covers satellites both for the owners and the manufacturers.

With complicated and technical operations, the role of insurance brokers and underwriters also increases in complexity. Too, financial institutions providing lending to Space businesses also often have additional stipulations on the insurance coverage and may even seek reinsurance. Reinsurance is a popular practice in high cost potential payouts wherein an insuring firm cedes a portion of the risk it is covering to share in both the premiums collected and the potential payout of an incident with a third-party. Although Space tourism is still in its infancy, it seems likely that insurance covering the liability of having human cargo involved more in the industry will also create new risks that will need to be underwritten. Space underwriter seems like a very cool and up and coming job title for tomorrow's job seekers.

The oldest name in Space insurance is Lloyd's. Lloyd's of London was involved with the underwriting and insurance of the first ever satellite policy in 1965. Lloyd's was also involved with the first satellite salvage mission in 1984. Privatization of the Space industry— and the growth of more firms devoted to commercial launch and satellite technology manufacturing —has created a complicated system of liabilities between the participant companies. Other companies involved with Space insurance include AIG, AXA XL, Allianz, Swiss Re, Munich Re, and others, each offering a unique suite of insurance products related to the industry. With the total number of commercial launches set to increase in the coming years, this increase in activity should lead to increased premium income to insurers. This increase in premium collection will likely cause an increase in interest in this sector and competition to reduce the premiums to Space businesses seeking insurance.

Using blockchain technology for Space insurance is something we are likely to see in the future. Although this might seem counterintuitive, improving transparency, resilience and real-time information can all improve premiums. Also, sound business practices and externalities that can generally not be easily captured can be tokenized and become inputs for gamification for internal compliance. Internal systems based around blockchain technology could more easily track issues and when events contribute to an insurable event the forensics possible under full transparency could lead to better risk, policy or preparedness in the future. It might also be able for firms to insure riskier enterprises, such as launch. If insurance firms had a fuller view into a riskier firms operation, this might lead to a mutually beneficial relationship. Another example of the role of blockchain in insurance is for helping identify products that fail a safety inspection or are subject to a recall. Insurance associated with specific parts or recalls risk is something firms must insure against for critical components. A firm that is better able to track issues that result in events or near insurable events based on recalls could more easily isolate what products were at issue and not need to destroy or replace entire batches. This could lead to both greater efficiencies for the firm and lower potential payouts by the insurance company. This type of system can be done both with enterprise and open solutions. It can also be done with advances in methods around how the insured and insurance provider interact using trusted oracles and smart contracts.

Lastly, blockchain based ownership of risk can help create new mutualization models. Insurance companies in general are classified as stock, mutual, or fraternal, based on the ownership of the firm. All of the companies we have talked about so far in Space insurance are stock or stakeholder owned where the goal is to make a profit. By comparison, a mutual or fraternal based insurance company operates where the policyholders directly share in the profits or losses of the company. In traditional finance, this is most closely relatable to the credit union model. (*The idea of credit unions for the Space industry deserves its own chapter but we will save that for another book.*) Typically, mutual insurance companies are managed by outside professional staff accountable to a board elected by members, and have the insurance company's assets, to include the float, kept for the benefit and protection of the insured. The float is the customer's money which the insurance company, mutual or stock, can invest for themselves until payment is expected by a policyholder, and this uniquely gives insurance companies a positive cost of capital. The future of the Space Economy includes insurance, and when we speak of risks in Space the list is long and insurance is one way to help with those lessen the impacts from those risks.

Private Firms need the opportunity for steady returns

Private firms in the Space economy or any industry need returns. Yes, this wisdom may seem old fashioned in the face of high-flying evaluations for technology companies that have gone for a decade or more without producing a profit, but it is still a fundamental truth of finance. The value of stocks, and in general any private enterprise, is based on the present value of future earnings. Most investors would be excited for guaranteed constant payouts, but those types of defined benefit pension plans died with the Employee Retirement Income Security Act of 1974 and the Pension Protection Act of 2006. *Quick aside, if ever you see legislation called the Space Economy Security Protection Act know that it is what is found on pages 400 to 600 that, despite the nice name, will stunt growth in the industry.*

The capture of returns and profits from private firms is part of a larger market made up of the risk-on versus risk-off trade. It is often talked about in finance and economics as a binary, but in truth, like most things, plenty of gray areas exist. The gray is where the risk professional lives and earns their keep. When the market— or in general uncertainty around a given asset class or project— is high this concern can translate to investment dollars leaving that sector or business. Think cruise ships and airlines after it became obvious that the Coronavirus was not going to just stay in Wuhan but had designs on spreading across the entire Earth. The largest event most often tied to the risk-off trade has to do with actions by the Federal Reserve to tighten interest rates. However, generally speaking it is a movement of money out of riskier investments into instruments considered to be closer to

114

risk-free, like US Treasury bonds or German bunds.

Steady returns most typically come from a mature and diversified business. Oftentimes investment professionals will cite the "Blue Chips" as stocks that are considered the best. Interestingly the term "blue chip" comes from gambling where at most casinos in the 1920s the blue tokens were the most valuable in poker, followed by white and then red. Investing still involves plenty of risk, and you should seek the advice of a professional who understands your risks, tolerances, and situation. Just keep in mind that investing is fundamentally regulated gambling. The "Blue Chip" name often comes with the connotation of financial stability, long-term growth records and a household brand name. It is also often used to refer specifically to the 30 stocks in the Dow (Dow Jones Industrial Average). Several firms that draw a portion of their revenue from the Space Economy are already Dow components, namely Boeing and United Technologies. United Technologies has been involved with Space as far back as the life support system, radio and fuel cell systems for the Apollo missions. Boeing has also been involved with Space since the beginning through its heritage companies, such as McDonnel Douglas, Hughes and Jeppesen. What is interesting is to think about and try to predict when a company that draws a majority of its income from Space will be a Dow component (our forecast says 2027 but please DYOR).

Steady returns come from a number of sources, and not all of them are around manufacturing. The future economy is one based on technology, innovation, and convergence. A large part of that economy revolves around invention, and the flexibility to deploy into dynamic markets that businesses both on Earth and in Space will need to operate. A critical part of this new structure is the ownership of intellectual property (IP). Space firms able to create breakthrough 5th Industrial Revolution technology must know that their IP rights will be protected to make the investments necessary to accomplish great scientific advancements.

$10,000 Dollar Arti'san Space Water is

usually Recycled Pee

Maybe the hardest to understand is the economic benefits from sheer expansion of Spaceports. It is likely we will see several dozen of these Spaceports in the next few decades. None of them will be self-sufficient in that time, if ever in our lifetime, so the goal should be to boost output and design a system of trade that supports multiple industries, technologies, and specializations. One example that can help in understanding this is the cost of a pint of water on the ISS, which at $10,000 puts even nightclub bottle service Dom' to shame. This cost stems from how expensive it is to get supplies up, with each run costing several million dollars. This puts cargo space at a premium, and places scrutiny on every item's weight, volume, and function.

The solution is to incentivize alternative providers of water from private space companies. Approximately every three months, 400 gallons of water has to be delivered for the astronauts, experiments, and systems of the ISS. If this doesn't seem like much water; that is because the station has a series of very efficient water harvesting and recycling systems that allow for 93% of the water on the station to be reclaimed from condensation, humidity, shower, and oral hygiene water, perspiration and urine. But even after all of this recycling, the water delivery alone is worth $32 Million every few months, and easily over $100Million each year. Who wants to be the Poland Springs of LEO?

Chapter 26 - What is the Space Economy about?

"The day before something is truly a breakthrough, it's a crazy idea."

- Peter Diamandis, XPrize Foundation-

L.E.O. (Low Earth Orbit), Satellites, Rocketry, Spaceports, the Moon, Mars, or asteroids. The fact is extant - Space has today (and will have in the future) major economic activity, involving the use and transfer of large sums of money. For now, the majority of that money is from state actors transferring it to the usual suspects in contracting, but as a competitive market system develops, with private corporations playing a larger and larger role, the total amount of product in Space will grow. Thanks to the increased presence of the competitive economic process, new activities will be tested, new businesses launched, and new ideas explored, those that add to total productivity will be successful, while those that don't will be rejected.

In this way, Space will mean different things to different organizations, businesses, and people.

- To telecom companies, Space will be the center of a growing communications universe because voice, data, and internet services will not be for one low price between Mars and Earth will force innovation and greater competition.
- To IT firms, Space will be a vast region from which more data can be harvested, managed, and analyzed.
- To healthcare and life sciences, Space will be a platform for breakthroughs in gene folding, new chemical molecules for medicine, and 3D-printing human organs.
- To manufacturing, the absence of gravity and the harshness of radiation will make way for brand new structures, designs, and materials.

117

- To retail where next day delivery will still be a big deal.
- To energy where water will be worth more per gallon than oil.
- To farming where not only new techniques will be experimented and developed, but likely even brand-new species of plants.
- To consulting where yes we will still be constantly trying to figure out how to best allocate scarce resources, minimize risks, and maximize profits.

The Space Economy is already here, with rockets and satellites as the fundamental building blocks, with space stations, drones on the moon, and 3D-printing materials for colonies completely underground or deep in craters or tubes. Just remember the importance of the Dunbar Number when calculating how many persons will be in these permanent habitats. The Space Force is going to be very busy protecting $Trillions$ in economic activity.

Extensions of Earth Businesses

In almost all cases, the change to businesses will not come as a separate or alternative way of doing business, but instead will be an extension and expansion of existing operations. Every business will have a Space operation. The value of those operations will be determined by the competitive nature of the economic activity taking place. Speaking of competition, we would like to reiterate that free private enterprise in Space will still operate based on an ordered system heavily influenced by governments here on Earth. Industrial nations with Space programs and those with the financial means to participate in launch with others or with private enterprise will have a large role to play in both the economic activity and the rules.

It is appropriate to think about the ownership and operation of potentially very large resources by governments with active involvement in Space. It also seems likely that governments will serve in a regulatory function relating to the ownership, acquisition, and allocation of resources just like they do here on Earth. Also, governments are likely to fill the gap in the provision of essential services and protection of wellbeing and protection of assets. Notwithstanding the superior productivity of free private enterprise, certain functions will remain government provided, albeit potentially by Space contractors.

So, what will these operations first produce and why? Or to put it a different way, which of these is game ready now? To measure the productivity of an economic system, we must look closely at the money spent. We will be able to forecast the money that will be spent based first off the identification of which opportunities to compete have clear advantages in Space. Those with the clear advantages, and therefore rewards, for businesses to pursue.

Chapter 27 - Drones in Space

A likely business sector candidate that has clear advantages in Space includes systems and networks that can organize the communication of drones. The US Department of Transportation has released details of their work and interest in using Blockchain and IoT, focusing on drone communication, and air traffic management. There are over 110,000 commercial drone operators in the US alone, and the ability to both regulate and innovate a nation's drone fleet is becoming an interesting domain. Analogous to some of the use cases we see around vehicle (autonomous or not) sharing sensor data (e.g. GM's recent patent on sensor inputs to maps, many of the MOBI use cases), there's an emerging demand for an underlying data sharing layer for drones. NASA is also developing a blockchain prototype for transmitting air traffic location data called the Automatic Dependent Surveillance-Broadcast to replace secondary surveillance radar.

Another application of drones is in the evolution of the manned-unmanned teaming experimentation by the US Navy that could also be applied to the Space Force. A technology created by Boeing allows the Navy to extend the reach of sensors and force, while keeping manned aircraft out of harm's way and simultaneously tripling airpower. RAND has reported that the Space Force is in need of significantly more people in order to fulfill its mission. Drone technologies multiply that force, particularly in places where it's expensive to operate, are very valuable. Pilots and operators coordinating in real-time will require imaginative communication technology and rapid processing of big data. Even as they are currently being developed for use on Earth, these attributable robotic elements' advancing capabilities and supporting operations will need advanced satellites, 5G, IoT and AI to achieve a trusted and fully integrated status. All of this has additional applications for research and support of DoD from businesses looking at the growing Space Economy.

Chapter 28 - Manufacturing in Space: ZBLAN, Made in Space™

Everything about Space is already interesting but, much like drones, when we see how it combines with something like fiber optics and 3D-printing, it is truly out of this world. ZBLAN (ZrF4-BaF2-LaF3-AlF3-NaF) is a specialty fiber optic that has up to 100 times lower signal loss than the silica glass (SiO2) that common fiber optics are made out of. Like all fiber optics, ZBLAN is small in diameter and uses light pulses to transmit information. The reason that this improvement in signal is so significant is that silica glass fiber optics depends on costly repeaters for use across long distances to boost the signal. The problem however, has been that when manufactured on Earth, ZBLAN forms microcrystals that make the fiber optics useless. Understanding that in Space, with the benefits of no convection and gravity, it could be produced, back in 2015 the Space Economy startup Made In Space manufactured ZBLAN via a specialty 3D-printer on the ISS. Made In Space has been awarded several NASA small business innovation grants (SBIR) over the years, since they were founded in 2010. Since 2015, the company has continued to work on projects aimed at commercialization in Space. Earth based traditional silicon fiber optics are a $7Billion dollar industry and in high demand, even with efficiency improvements of tenfold and not the theoretical 100 times better ZBLAN could be. It could be one of the first drivers for the development of a private space station dedicated to manufacturing products for use on Earth. The CEO of Made In Space, Andrew Rush, is a well-respected advocate for greater public-private partnerships in Space, based on his own experience with the structure and benefits of that type of system

"If we will not endure a king as a political power, we should not endure a king over the production, transportation, and sale of any of the necessaries of life." -US Senator John Sherman

As we envision the potential future of manufacturing in Space, we should also reflect on the important role small and medium size companies play in innovation and ensure that access and mechanisms to support them are in place. Advanced manufacturing in Space could pass satellites as the biggest reason to go to Space. It does not have to be manufacturing dominated by monopolies as we have seen in previous Industrial Revolutions. With the ability for players both big and small to access Space for technological advancement and ultimately commercialization of products; after just a few innovations like ZBLAN we could see a booming manufacturing community in Space contributing to the Trillion dollar economy over our heads. For all of these future products, like ZBLAN, they will have to be worth the cost of sending materials up and bringing finished products down. These private space stations or larger combination facility spaceports can be expected to use advanced autonomous robotics in manufacturing and assembly platforms.

Chapter 29 - 4D Printing

Recently scientists from MIT have used temperature signals to take 3D-printing to another level and add a "D" for deform. The adaptable structures go from a flat sheet into a complex structure and back again in response to a change in temperature. If this same mechanism was adapted to respond to say a specific electrical signal, the applications for Space construction could be enormous. It could also have applications for adapting structures made out of the material on a regular basis making possible flex-construction, or structure adaptive spaces. On Earth, we could see how the ability for a large structure to shift from one state to another to serve irregular or rare demand would be very valuable. An example would be sports stadium seating built with this material (and always out of the pockets of local taxpayers) that could transform into family pods for disaster housing. Like origami, the material uses a mesh-like lattice structure for the printing. The lattice is made out of a rubbery material that expands when the temperature increases. The gaps in the lattice make it easier for the material to adapt and reach large surface areas with incredible flexibility. This is not currently something ready for the Space Economy, and it may never come to fruition, but it is still an example of the types of advances in material science to look for that have cross applications.

Chapter 30 - Recycling, Solar & Circular Economies

In Space, the important and cool things to do will still be solar and recycling. ESG investing— which stands for environmental, social impact and governance investing— has come into popularity in recent years and was of late a major focus of the World Economic Forum in Davos. The Forum's mission states that it is, "committed to improving the state of the world by engaging business, political, academic, and other leaders of society to shape global, regional, and industry agendas." The annual event in Davos is a hot-bed of activity, and often compared by conspiracy theorists as akin to the Illuminati, Skulls, or Bilderberg, but even without the rumors of the occult it is still an interesting and hugely important economic meeting to watch.

Among investments and technologies promoted out of the Forum most recently has been ESG; and both solar power and recycling technologies here on Earth have practical applications in the Space economy. Solar sails are a fascinating concept, and one that has been demonstrated by the Planetary Society's LightSail missions. Another area of solar power still being researched is the efficiency of photovoltaic cells on the Moon for bases there and it also shows great promise. Space solar cells used by the ISS are different from those used on Earth, but have led to many improvements of the technology and of batteries. The solar arrays on the ISS consists of four sections that together produce about twice the amount of power needed by the station. This system was designed, tested and manufactured here on Earth two decades ago.

Also interesting is that at this same time, scientific research is underway that is pushing the 50% efficiency barrier commonly viewed as a wall for solar panels. The standard silicon limit based on single-junction solar cells is 33%, and by comparison you or your neighbor's roof panels are only about 15% efficient; that is if you are lucky and they are being kept clean. This is a gigantic leap forward in efficiency, and although it is not yet commercially viable, it potentially paves the way for very interesting new economies around solar energy here on Earth.

Solar energy in Space also has an interesting path ahead. As previously mentioned, energy is always an important part of an economy, and the Space economy will be no different. One way that markets for electricity are changing here on Earth is with smart grids, so a natural question is, what does a smart grid look like in Space? It might seem obvious that with the cost of running lines and transmitting electricity 220miles above the Earth it is prohibitively expensive, but perhaps other technologies can be combined to create an environmentally and economically viable system. One way might be the use of a Space elevator. When attempting to picture a Space elevator, think of the type of structure Brad Pitt falls off of in Ad Astra (although that structure was more of a ladder and would have mass problems but it gives you an idea). Another way is to use lasers to beam solar power from satellites in orbit down to Earth for electricity.

A community of spacecraft and space stations will use IoT technology for all devices, blockchain enabled SADA systems, micropayment networks for balancing, ceramic nanoparticles for battery storage, and more technology still being researched and developed today. All this activity and advanced systems from multiple actors will require greater power demands. Another area of power in Space is the likely market development of orbital drones that can function as storage, charging, and refueling envoys. As previously mentioned, power lines in Space would obviously not be practical, so instead of lines like we use in terrestrial infrastructure we would use a system of these drones. The cost of solar energy in Space is cheap, but the cost of not having energy is high. A Speedway drone swarm collecting solar energy and being contracted to refuel satellites and spaceports does not seem a big stretch of the imagination. The end of the useful life of many satellites is due to it running out of enough propellant to maintain an orbit, but with the proper engineering these satellites could be refueled keeping them running economically for longer.

Chapter 31 - Space Trash

An additional use of these solar drones would be to collect Space trash. Space trash, litter and debris will continue to grow until solutions are put into place to both collect and prevent its exponential growth. Millions of pieces are currently just floating around in LEO. This orbital litter is mainly made of paint from spacecraft, parts of rockets, or remains of objects that have hit each other at high speeds creating still more debris. As the number of pieces increases, the number of collisions also increases, and a runaway version of this chain-reaction can lead to what is known as Kessler Syndrome. These bits, pieces, and objects in orbit flying around at high speeds of 20,000 mph are the largest risk to satellites and spacecraft, because, even when small pieces hit, damage can be significant and trash of only a few centimeters in size would have the damaging effect equivalent to multiple sticks of dynamite exploding.

The first step in the problem with Space trash has been the creation of a space surveillance network. This is currently done via Earth-based ground stations to track larger pieces of space trash; in the hopes of avoiding collisions with satellites and spacecraft. The problem is being actively studied by numerous researchers and universities. Some ideas include better coatings and engineering so that smaller pieces, paint and parts don't break off and contribute on such a regular basis to the growing problem.

Another issue is the testing of ASAT (anti-satellite) weapons by the USA, Russia, India, and China, that has added to the debris in Space. Other plans look to create a cooperative effort between governments to stop the littering and build cleanup programs. This mission and these cleanup programs are also being pursued by private firms looking to profit from being the Waste Management of Space. The problem of all of these systems is linked to a concept in economics known as **"The Tragedy of The Commons"** which states that with any shared resource, each individual actor has an incentive to consume at the expense of all other actors. This type of behavior for a shared resource will result in overconsumption, under investment, and eventually the depletion of the resource. What is troubling in the navigability of Space near Earth is its just such a shared resource. Perhaps one way to overcome this would be to supply a profit motivation for the removal of Space trash. As the expression goes, "it's a dirty job[20] but someone's gotta do it." A company, or group of firms, could be paid to clean up Space and this will certainly become a profitable enterprise if the market pays the fair value of this service. But how do we get the market to pay for this service? Taxes collected on Space launches is one way to pay for it.

.

---

[20] We cannot wait to see Mike Rowe in full astronaut gear on the Space edition of Dirty Jobs.

Chapter 32 - Commodity Trading on the Moon

"Life is pain, your highness. Anyone that says differently is selling something." - Dread Pirate Roberts, The Princess Bride

Competitive economic systems are free from any individual or organization singularly responsible for what, how, or for whom to produce, which supports a free pricing mechanism. Space doesn't work that way.

The free pricing mechanism serves to balance consumer demand and production. Having things at the right place at the right time is another important part of economic systems, as the ebbs and flows of wants, needs, and supplies will fluctuate. Again, if we are honest about the starting form of the Space Economy, or any other new market, we can see that this idealized form will not be how things begin. Excepting this initial lack of pure competition and understanding the opportunities it provides is also a center of much potential profit.

An element of this initial competitive economic system will be the ability of individual actors to exert market power and influence on price, or what we more commonly refer to as monopoly power. As we think about the Space Economy, we can clearly see how initially many of the conditions of a perfectly competitive market will not be present.

Conditions of Perfectly Competitive Markets:

(1) large numbers of buyers and sellers,

(2) homogeneous products,

(3) full information,

(4) independence of operations,

(5) free entry and exit from the market[21].

Firms who are early to the market will benefit from large scale operations that can operate before these competitive market conditions are present. One of the areas that we already see the problem with the lack of these conditions here on Earth is mining and rare earths.

---

[21] This list is also a good starting point for the consideration of other markets and structures around other areas of the economy outside of Space, such as: media, healthcare and big tech. In classical economic theory or free market economics the systems of the economy are seen as largely self-regulating and capable of achieving full output and employment without government interference or fiscal policy. An important note here is that to be truly Smithian (a follower of Adam Smith's economic principles) you must also appreciate how he saw enlightened self-interest and freedoms' role in economic activity. To simplify without each of the conditions of a perfectly competitive market achieved government has a role to play to help the invisible hand. While a deeper dive is outside of the scope of this book please recognize this list as a helpful tool in your own analysis of markets and economic systems in the future be they Earth or Space based.

Chapter 33 - Rare Earths 101

Planetary Resources and Deep Space Industries both recently pursued the mining of asteroids and other operations have also discussed the mining and industrialization of the Moon. The reason that many of these firms have failed is because, while identifying the opportunities may be easy, Space is expensive, and Space is hard. Sometimes to succeed in the face of cost and difficulty, the answer is partnerships. For years now the US and other nations have talked about the problem with limited access to crucial rare earth supplies outside of China. Rare earths are crucial for the supply chain of medical, green energy, laptops, phones, electronic manufacturers, and Space firms. The demand for rare earth magnets alone has increased by double digits for the past several years.

Malaysia, Australia, Namibia, and Canada also have rare earth supplies; but over 85% of most of the 15 lanthanides, plus scandium and yttrium that the material and divides are modern world is built on comes from just one place, China. Importantly, mining is not the only way to get them. Rare earth nodules have also been discovered on the seabed near Hawaii. However, harvesting them is still very controversial given the potential environmental impacts. Speaking of the environment, coal ash processing is also a source of rare earths. No one likes to talk about coal any more, but to be fair, we use coal for about 25% of our electricity in the US, and that percentage is much higher in some nations. A byproduct of burning coal is ash, and the US produces 80 million tons of it each year. Currently, a bit less than half of it is used for an ingredient in cement and to enrich soil with macro and micronutrients for farming. The rest, sadly, goes to landfills, or gets mixed with water and put in open ground pit containment ponds. However, those landfills and ponds contain reasonable amounts of rare earths like scandium and neodymium. Additionally, recycling is also a great source of rare earths. When economists speak of a new circular economy they don't speak of rare earths, but rare earths are a great example of the type of resource that would do well in those systems.

Texas also has rare earths, and a recent huge discovery of them in Round Top holds the promise of making America largely rare earth self-sufficient. The mountain east of El Paso contains cerium, lanthanum, praseodymium (essential to advanced engines in aerospace) & neodymium, along with deposits of heavy rare earths, like dysprosium (EV hybrid cars) and the permanent magnets family of metals. It will be exceedingly hard to compete in the Fourth Industrial Revolution without rare earths, and IMPOSSIBLE to participate in the Fifth Industrial Revolution without them.

Chapter 34 - Space Mining

As the great bard Shakespeare taught us in The Merchant of Venice, "all that glitters is not gold" because sometimes what is attractive is not valuable. Gold will not be valuable in Space as it is far too common when compared to Latinum. When a large amount of precious metals from Space is introduced to supplies here on Earth, the impact is interesting to consider. We will get into that a bit later on when we make some predictions on what's ahead for the Space economy. In the meantime, keep in mind, the total amount of samples ever collected from the Moon as we examine space mining. Over the course of the six Apollo missions from 1962-to-1972, the US brought back 382kg (842lbs) of lunar rock, core samples, pebbles, sand, and dust accounting for over 2,000 different individual samples.

Precious metals and strategic metals, of which rare earths is a part, include things like platinum, gold, and silver but also specialty metals like the ones in LEDs, sensors, satellites, rockets and nuclear power. Nuclear power in the Space economy is also a fascinating topic next time, but until then it is an important subject to start following. Excluding precious metals for a moment; comparing the less than half ton of Space rocks ever collected to the over 4,500 tons of rare earth magnet shipments that came into the US last year alone gives you a very conservative scope and scale of the potential demand and ability for a firm dedicated to Space mining to capture this opportunity.

Space mining in general seems likely to take one of three avenues. The first is a traditional, albeit very high tech and risky operation, to establish mining on the Moon. Silicon for example is very plentiful and could be mined, refined, and manufactured all in situ (on site) for solar panels. Titanium is also present as ilmenite, which happily also includes iron and oxygen, so refining it might be useful for its byproducts alone. Aluminum is also plentiful on the Moon, and a potential valuable mineral for building permanent structures. Also, we cannot forget about water in the form of ice in craters and the Moons polls.

The second avenue for Space mining is what we will refer to as Garbage Mining. Yes, this is a bit of a "cheat", but the concept is important and the term needs to catch on as much on Earth as it will in Space. Everything has value in Space— from pee to popsicle sticks to decommissioned satellites— and as systems develop around maximizing the recycling and reuse of these materials, Garbage Mining will be a major contributor to the Space economy.

Last, and the type of mining everyone loves to talk about the most (made famous by Bruce Willis in Armageddon), is asteroid mining. Now, technically they were drilling an asteroid to explode it before it could impact Earth, but the visuals, antics, and actions are iconic of popular sci-fi conversations around asteroid mining. NASA landed on the asteroid Eros almost twenty years ago, circled and took thousands of photos and measurements, and collected large amounts of data, growing our knowledge of asteroids. More recently, JAX landed on Ryugu and collected samples that are due back to Earth soon.

Space mining is a logistics problem as much as it is a technological one. As transportation costs to and in Space decline it will cause a reduction in marginal costs of things like cobalt and platinum, and other minerals that can be mined from asteroids, and launched back to Earth. Once back near Earth the question would become is it more cost effective for minerals to be processed and sent down or used for in-orbit manufacturing and construction projects. As the industry develops it likely quickly reaches a point where the economics favor materials mined from asteroids to be used in Space to those products and materials launched from the Earth. Some even theorize a future where the Earth's resources are preserved in favor of mining off the planet. While any future like this seems a long way off it is important to appreciate the logistics involved and efficient systems likely to develop around the "highways of space." Space mining operations will have food and supplies shipped to them and in those same containers millions if not billions of dollars in valuable minerals will be returned. For anyone from Texas this should sound reminiscent of the oil and gas industry towns of the 20th century. Likewise, or anyone from Maine very similar to the logging operations and towns in the 19th century that were started around firms and workers devoted to the exploration, development, and extraction of resources. The question, therefore, is where will the next Houston or Bangor be in the Space economy?

While all this activity involving asteroids is a start to the mining of their contents, it still appears to be farther away than the mining of the Moon for resources needed in the construction of bases and permanent settlements there. As launch costs come down, our ability to put more things in orbit increases, but the technology to travel out into deep space is still not commercialized. This year we will see the first delivery of astronauts to the ISS by a commercial firm when SpaceX does so with NASA using the Dragon Crew vehicle on top of a Falcon rocket. While impressive and an extension of the delivery of cargo, food and supplies via commercial launch, we have seen for years now neither of these capabilities is the same as going out and landing or capturing an asteroid for mining. Without question, asteroid mining is an area of continued interest and development in the Space economy, as the imagination is certainly already in place. At this point, it is just a matter of the technology and economics catching up to make it a reality.

Chapter 35 - National Moon Bases

"Silent and sparkling, bright and baleful, those moon-cursed waters hurried I knew not whither." - H.P. Lovecraft, What the Moon Brings

The Moon has been the jumping off point to our understanding of the solar systems, and ourselves, for millennia. Moon worship is recorded throughout ancient history with great prominence, and is second only to the deification of the Sun. Nibosit Gizos or "night walker sun" is part of Penobscot Native American beliefs, and in many other cultures harvest moons and solstice moons are celebrated or have slipped into syncretism with modern holidays. After landing on the Moon in the 1960s, the relationship with Her has changed. Once we were able to take that "One small step for man; one giant leap for mankind" we proceeded to do science experiments, collect rocks (400kg of samples), drive cars, hit golf balls, and consider developing malls and shopping centers on her surface. But after all that we didn't go back. Everyone has a theory why, and some of them are better than others, but the easiest and correct answer is lack of economic incentives.

We have used the technology we developed back then to push ourselves to send satellites to every planet in our solar system and 40+ orbiters, landers, and rovers to Mars. But the last time humans were on the Moon it was Eugene Cernan, commander of Apollo 17, at 17:55 EST on December 14th, 1972. Now, we have the capability to go to the Moon again and send astronauts to Mars, but this time we don't have the political motivations.

The first Space Race was mostly driven by a political purpose in the Cold War, that being an expression of scientific, military, and economic superiority. Now don't get us wrong, political purposes can create economic incentives, we call those subsidies. Subsidies come about, often, due to lobbying, and for this reason, previous economic research has shown an ROI on lobbying to be around **20,000%**. Yes, you read that correctly. The next closest example of those types of returns would be buying the pizza for

Laszlo Hanyecz in 2010 and him giving you 10,000 bitcoin that you HODL.

That the political will to go back to the Moon is important, but more important this time is the pure economic incentives involved. *A lunar base will be established in the next decade* and of that we are certain. The only question is: will it be the US, another nation, or a private company who runs it? Unlike the Apollo missions, going to the Moon this time will be to establish a permanent base and eventual permanent human settlement.

The concepts for a Moon base have been around for decades, but this time when it happens it will be for the benefit of the larger Space Economy, and not just pursued as an exercise in national pride. A clear economic reason must be articulated. Some of the science, manufacturing, and tourism activities already discussed for space stations or spaceports are also possible on the Moon. Because of the short time lag to the Moon, much like spaceports, robots/drones could be operated easily from Earth to augment inhabitants' labor who are part of our permanent presence there.

Whoever goes to the Moon first, this time, will have more of a voice in the Moon's future than people who haven't been for fifty years. Yes, that might have just made you a bit uncomfortable, and it should. Let's look at each of these possible scenarios in a bit more detail.

It is well within the technological and economic abilities of the United States to return to the Moon and set up a base. The difference is this time we are not in a Cold War. Sure, we are in a cyber battle every day, but we don't classify it as a New Cold War. We need the political will to do the hard things, and open competition to be the first to establish a permanent Moon base is just that.

Chapter 36 - Moon Mission the Sequel - This Time It's Personal

What's different this time is that the field of potential other powers on Earth with the capabilities to also get to the Moon and establish a permanent base has gotten much bigger and wider. The short list of other countries (or political unions) that have ever been to or orbited the Moon would include: Russia, Japan, China, EU-European Space Agency, India, Israel, and Luxembourg. Now to be fair, not all of these were successful, and some "hopped" rides with other nations but it is a good list to start with.

Chapter 36a - Russia Zvezda Two

The Soviets originally had plans in the 1960s and 1970s to build a manned moonbase constructed of modules, uniform in size, that could be connected together on the surface to hold a crew of around 10 cosmonauts. Fast forward to the late 1980s, and Soviet engineers had completed the Energia rocket, which, at almost 200 feet (60 meters), was widely regarded as the most advanced and powerful rocket of its time, and when combined with the reusable Buran was built as a rival to the Shuttle. However, when the USSR fell in 1991, the Energia was left to rot, with its advanced hydrogen engines, in a hangar in the Baikonur Cosmodrome in present day Kazakhstan. The design for the moon base, like the capabilities of the Energia and Buran, were lost.

In October of 2005, however, Russian President Vladimir Putin reversed this trend by placing major investments back into the Roskosmos (Russian Space Agency) program. Also, during this period, the US signaled it was no longer interested in international cooperation for the ISS, and that it planned to withdraw, focusing instead on domestic built capabilities for future American lunar missions. Cooperation on future missions, to include a mission to the Moon, looked promising until the War in Georgia in 2008, and the escalation of tensions between Europe and Russia.

According to the long-term planning of the Russian Space program— and public announcements— manned missions to the Moon could take place between 2025 and 2030, followed by an expedition to Mars by the 2035-2040 time period. In this way, Russia has a clear advantage over efforts from other nations that might change every few years with political shifts.

The ability to think long-term in Space is always an advantage over anyone playing a short game, because it is not ballistics, but inertia that moves things in Space.

Russia also has the advantage of being part of the partnership, renewed since the icy relationships in the early 2000s, around the ISS now focusing efforts on the Deep Space Gateway (DSG). The project's goal is to lead human exploration into deep space, including a return to the Moon, visits to asteroids, and a mission to Mars. Ruskosmos has also been reported to be in the midst of planning for its own space station before the ISS reaches its next continued operations evaluation and potential retirement.

Russian ambitions for a Moon base seem likely for a number of reasons. First, they have a long and proud history of success in Space, and the stomach for the inevitable setbacks that come with big, high-risk high-reward missions. The economics also makes sense because it provides an industry for the nation to support that will diversify earnings, activity, and research away from dependency on the oil markets. The political policy benefits, implications and leverage also makes sense in securing Russia's position as a global power in the next century, with permanent operations on the lunar surface.

Chapter 37 - European Union Moon Village(s)

The EU option is a proposal to not go it alone, but is instead more akin to an international option, similar to the concept behind the ISS but on the Moon. This might come in many different flavors, but it is what the ESA (European Space Agency) has previously proposed with their "Moon Village." The idea is to create something like a community of cooperative entities on the Moon, all located around a village-like center. The advantage of this project is that groups can join forces, barter for resources among each other, and support each other with individual capabilities. The term "village" also refers to the idea of people coming together with shared interest without necessarily having all the details worked out.

Part of the discussion around the Moon Village is also related to the vision and plans for continued activities for Mars, the asteroid belt, and Deep Space. Many believe that the Moon is the best place to first test out new technologies, systems, and approaches to push us out into the rest of the Solar System. Equally important, however, is the benefits felt on Earth from all of this activity. The ESA, like NASA, has an active technology transfer program that promotes commercialization of things like advanced drones, extreme temperature devices, high grade antennas, and many more inventions first designed, created and used by ESA.

The Moon Village also seeks to provide fascination and inspiration to young people, and spark an interest in STEM subjects. This integration of Space with education initiatives is very important and also part of several other plans. The ability to bring parties together to coordinate and create synergies is something the EU prides itself on, and is something that will be necessary for a successful Moon Village.

Not wanting to step on international toes, it seems appropriate to also highlight that France, Germany, and the UK have the capabilities separately for a Moon mission and base. Also, on the subject of separate, Caldonia merits a mention on this list. Caldonia, or Scotland if you prefer, has both native private Space companies like Orbex, which seeks to use carbon-fiber to 3D-print rockets, and government economic and community development agencies like Highlands and Islands Enterprise (HIE) for multiple Spaceports under various stages and steps in consideration. In light of Brexit and of other political tensions it is important to simply mention these as other potential names on the list to also separately add to the nations on the Moon.

Chapter 38 – China's Moon Base

China will definitely have a Moon base and maybe it will be the first.

Chapter 39 – Moon Base India

India has ambitious plans for Space and the Moon. They have spent decades planning and developing their Space industry and are also well positioned for a Moon base not long after the Chinese. The ISRO is famous for its ability to do things in Space at less than a tenth (or in some cases even less) the cost of what other Space programs are spending to do similar things. This also earns them sharp criticism and quick attention when they have failures, like what happened with their last moon rover. The more important point is that with a fraction of the budget they are doing similar Space engineering, research, and development as the USA, Russia, China, the Europeans and Japan. Sometimes the economics of how a system works comes out of necessity.

Human space-flight missions are currently slated for 2021 and we will watch closely the progress of the program and the astronauts' voyage. The Indians have already sent missions to Mars back in 2014, doing so for under $75Million, and considering the pace at which they are moving, Elon might have some competition; or more likely a valuable trading partner for his own base. Also, ISRO has recently announced the process for the creation and construction of a second spaceport in the southern port city of Thoothukudi.

Many have quietly projected for the past decade that it is India and not China that the world should be paying attention to as the growing power in Asia. India is predicted to take top spot as the most populous country in the world by the mid-2020s, and it has the fifth largest GDP (third if you look at purchasing power parity). Much like the US, India has both large farm and factory output, both sectors that take advantage of significant technologies transferable to building successful Space economy firms. India is a country to watch and a space station and Moon base in the near term both seem very likely achievements.

Chapter 40 – Moon Base Japan

Japan has a long history in Space technology development, and particularly rocketry, stretching back over fifty years. The development of torpedo bombers that could be used in the shallow waters of Pearl Harbor on December 7th, 1941, and the use of the Baka (Kamikaze rocket planes) in World War II— while both deadly— were clear demonstrations of early advanced engineering prowess. After the war, and most interesting in the early years of the non-military and pure scientific development, was the Pencil Rocket in 1955. Created by Prof Itokawa of the University of Tokyo, the Pencil Rocket is a famously small rocket that at only 23cm (9inches) was the world's smallest rocket; engineered at a time when most other scientists were focused on larger and larger systems. This development led to the Japanese Kappa family of rockets, which in the late 1950s and early 1960s, eventually reached heights of 200km, breaking past the Kármán line and into Space, becoming among the first to do so. This provided advantages and a head start for the early development and deployment of satellites.

Since then, Japan has made steady progress in launch technology. They established the National Space Development Agency (the predecessor of JAXA), and opened the Tanegashima Space Center in 1969, also among the first to establish an agency and launch center for future Space development. Following their defeat in World War II, the Japanese were not permitted a military, and the focus they put on Space in the absence of applications for warfare is unique and interesting, as it provides a very pure example of the economic pursuits alone behind the early growth in the industry. In this same vein, the first Japanese astronaut was a journalist who took part in a space flight in 1990 aboard a Soviet Soyuz spacecraft to the Mir space station. When looking at the Space Economy and economic systems of development, cooperation, and trade the Japanese have been at it for a long time.

The Japanese are world leaders in the field of asteroid exploration through the Hayabusa first mission in 2003 and second in 2014. Hayabusa 2 is scheduled to return in late 2020 from the asteroid Ryūgū. The samples and information Hayabusa 2 has collected from this asteroid have the potential to further escalate the interest in commercial asteroid mining.

Japan has also sent scientific probes to both Mars and Venus. Recently they also successfully launched a cargo transporter to the ISS, their seventh, as part of a program that stretches back to 2009. For the cargo missions, JAXA has used commercial firm Mitsubishi Heavy Industries, whose H-IIB rocket is unmanned and able to deliver 4tons of supply to the ISS, as the prime contractor. Another large commercial firm, Sony, has been testing laser-communications terminals for future communications between satellites, ground stations, and eventually Earth, the Moon, and Mars. The ultra-fast laser communication technology is significant because today most transmissions rely on radio waves, which have a far more limited bandwidth for sending information. More information transmission capabilities means more value from satellites already in orbit, and the thousands scheduled for future launches, allowing them to send more data back to Earth.

Specific to its Moon missions, JAXA has plans to create a moon base with the use of autonomous robots. The idea is, with the two second radio delay for communications between the Earth and the Moon, the robots can work largely on their own in constructing component pieces and will require little human supervision. This is similar to projects launched by NASA to develop and launch an autonomous space robot that can manufacture and assemble itself and other materials in orbit. In comparison to the development and research into potential applications from several private firms in the US, the role of humans back on Earth to pilot for JAXA is minimal, with a much larger focus on pure autonomous operations, even though the development and research are similar. These systems are generally referred to as Robotics and Autonomous Systems (RAS), and have a long history made famous by the Freeman Dyson Astrochicken's thought experiment in his book "Disturbing the Universe" and the self-replicating malevolent depictions in Sci-Fi like the Replicators insect robot race in

Stargate.

JAXA has been researching Space RAS applications for over three years now in collaboration with Kajima Corp, a Japanese construction firm, and several national universities. The task of building a Moon base for humans using autonomous robots is focused on many of the early stage tasks that would be most difficult for astronauts. The RAS project is focused on handling remotely from Earth things like site preparation, excavation, and installation of habs and radiation shielding, to make the role of humans on the Moon less hazardous when they arrive to finish or augment construction tasks. Having a partially constructed base already in place will make the jobs of astronauts easier and safer at the same time.

The large multinational Japanese based vehicle manufacturer Toyota is also involved with the Space economy. They are currently focused on work to create a new moon rover to transport humans around the lunar surface. JAXA hopes to have its astronauts on the Moon in the 2030s, and as briefly summarized includes cooperation with a large number of domestic firms and universities with a strong focus on commercialization and scientific research.

Chapter 41 – Moon Base *New Jerusalem*

Israel has local launch capabilities, so it is on the aforementioned list. They have built a Space agency whose mission includes building partnerships, promoting ties for scientific exploration, and support of their satellite industry, so although they are a likely member of a multinational effort, they seem unlikely to go to the Moon alone at this time. The Israel Space Agency (ISA) was founded in 1983 and is responsible for coordinating the scientific and technological activities of the civilian space program. At that time, ISA was only the eighth nation on Earth to put a satellite into Space. The agency is particularly interested in Space related activities that contribute to the Israeli economy, and within this mission they promote academic sector research and invest in start-ups.

Israel also has focused programs in satellites and miniaturization. This has given them a sizable competitive advantage in the booming industry of remote sensing, imagery and communication. Israel also focuses educational efforts on the engineering of these technologies and has developed partnerships with schools and universities domestically to continue to promote these disciplines in the next generation of scientists. A number of firms are currently working on smallsat, microsatellites and nano-satellites in the country, with emphasis on high resolution photographic capabilities from LEO and communication satellites in GEO.

Israel also operates a fleet of satellites for itself to include: the Amos communication array composed of five satellites, two Eros photography satellites, and several research satellites. As recently as last year, news reports of anomalies and disruptions to GPS for Israeli pilots have raised the question of whether Israel might also deploy its own global navigation satellite system. Given the nation's safety concerns, and its expertise with satellites, it seems that this would be something they could easily deploy as a redundancy or augmentation to existing capabilities.

Also, given the strength of the Israeli presence in the satellite industry, it is likely that Moon-based systems for navigation will potentially be engineered and supplied by firms in the country, giving them a foothold in dialogues and conversations around cooperation for any Moon base.

Chapter 42 – Dubai Luna

The UAE Space Agency is very active and has a uniquely comprehensive and fast-growing presence in the space sector. It certainly should be considered a center of local launch capabilities for the Middle East, but also deserves recognition for its partnership with multiple nations and participation and planning around ambitious projects like its Mars 2117 Project. They have built a truly formidable space agency in a relatively short amount of time that has focused not only on infrastructure but also on policy development for legal frameworks for firms looking to operate in the Space Economy.

It is also important to note that the UAE has directed resources at knowledge transfer and education programs that are building a pipeline of engineers, scientists, and researchers for the sector. This directive to focus and build a strong pipeline of talent includes specific programming, attention, and teaching at the Sharjah University and the National Space Science and Technology Center (NSSTC) at UAE University. In partnership with Boeing, the UAE education initiatives in Space also got a boost with a recent mini satellite STEM program that brought in participants from around the Middle East. These strategies demonstrate a willingness to play a very long game and that is what is needed for success in Space.

The UAE has also positioned itself as a leader for satellites and communication in the Middle East, but also has entered markets to provide services in parts of Africa and Asia. The UAE satellite and communication networks operate within the company's Yahsat for internet and broadcast TV, and Thuraya for cellular telephone services. In 2018, the Mohammed bin Rashid Space Center (MBRSC), think of it as the Rocket City Huntsville Alabama of the Emirates, had the successful launch of its first satellite built and engineered entirely in the UAE. Also, of note, the astronaut program sent its first Emirati to the ISS last year. Given all these factors, a base by the UAE on the Moon seems inevitable.

Chapter 43 – Luna Luxembourg

Luxembourg is unlikely to set up the first Moon base. This prediction is based on the objectives of their space agency to act as a collaborating force for private enterprise and allocate the nation's space fund of $100 million Euros towards public-private partnerships for new technology in the space economy. This is an important role for a nation to play in Space Race 3.0, but it is not likely a formula to be the first nation with a flag on the door of a Moon hab. But as previously mentioned in our conversation about how the current Space Economy is predominantly focused on satellites in LEO, it is worth noting that Luxembourg has over thirty satellites in orbit: putting it in the top ten of all nations.

Chapter 44 – North Nigeria

Nigeria has not been part of a mission to orbit the Moon, but Lagos, the capital of Nigeria, is estimated to be the largest city on Earth by 2100. It stands to reason that the nation will also have a role in the Space Economy and potentially the Moon. Already, it is the largest city in Africa, and the center of a considerable amount of trade and business for the region. Unlike some nearby nations it is located on the Atlantic coast, and has a diversified, non-oil dependent economy with prosperous manufacturing, transportation, construction, service, and retail sectors. Many of the businesses in these sectors are leaders and gateways to the rest of the markets in Africa. In many industries and sectors, Africa has shown an ability to apply technologies, like mobile phones and laptops, to leapfrog and foster rapid economic growth.

Honorable Mentions

Ukraine, Hungary, Brazil, Argentina, South Africa, and Australia are all likely to also get to Moon landing technology in our lifetimes and position themselves for cooperation on international Moon bases.

Chapter 45 - FarmTech in Space

"You can tell you've found a really interesting question when nobody wants you to answer it." -Miller, The Expanse

Elon Musk has almost all of the components of Space spread across his various companies. Besides the obvious SpaceX we also must consider the battery technology of Tesla, and the solar cell applications of SolarCity. Next is the Boring Company digging tunnels in California, and the Las Vegas Convention Center, which has a great future use case for the construction of structures under the service of the Moon or Mars. He also has the vacuum tubes for rapid transit or, applied slightly differently, the beginnings of a railgun that could put supplies on the Moon or blast supplies out from an industrialized Moon to ships nearby headed to Mars, since they would be more efficient than launches.

But the one facet that isn't listed but should be obvious to anyone is farmtech, and this is a miss. Even small misses in Space are big deals, so we have already provided this chapter to everyone with emails ending "@spacex.com" we could think of, but if you think we missed someone please let them know for us. The Milky Way Economy has plenty of other ideas about the intersection of farmtech an   d Space, but just to be clear, this intersection is of great import for one very simple reason - everyone has to eat.

Currently, rations are sent up to feed the crews, but it would be nice for farmtech to help astronauts grow their own food. This is more than just a nice to have, this is an economics question around the cost to transport food to Space versus the cost to grow it there. Note, this is also a call to action for Space Entrepreneurs, especially those in the cannabis space with the green thumb expertise to grow leafy green plants in enclosed environments.

Thanks to the movie *The Martian*, we all know that potatoes do well in Space. It is unlikely that Dr. Whatney had potatoes selected for their drought resistant or storage capabilities, or he would have had Maine heirloom Katahdin potatoes. Needless to say, we still have a long way to go in figuring out where, how, and what to grow for plants in Space. Seeds were first shot into space in the late 1940s aboard V-2 rockets to include corn, rye, and cotton for radiation experiments. Apollo 14 also took seeds with it around the Moon from trees that were later planted, grown and studied to observe for any effects.

Actual growth of seeds in Space was first done aboard the last of the Salyut stations. Given the small size of only 100cu meters, is it a testament to the vital importance of plant research that a micro-greenhouse was placed there and included in the mission. More recently, China conducted experiments around growing cotton on the far side of the Moon in 2019. The seed did produce a leaf but the conditions on the Moon, even with the special biosphere equipment, proved too hard for the plant that had been attached to the Chang'e-4 mission probe. The importance of both of these is clear, the US, Russia and China all realize that if we want to live long term away from Earth, we will have to take along with us some of the plants that keep us alive.

Green Thumbs in Space use 3D-Printers

It is for this reason that a green thumb in Space will both be a reference to the life-giving plants Space gardeners will grow, but also as a throwback to an earlier time when money was green. Money in Space will certainly not be green, but we will save that for a later chapter. So, how do we become good gardeners in Space? Without getting into the physiological effects of gravity on plants, and the numerous experiments being conducted on the subject, the simple answer is research, technology and practice.

A good thing about growing plants in Space is that light is not an issue. The light of the sun reaches satellites in orbit, future space stations, and the Moon all equally well. Also, the use of red/blue/green LED lights makes it possible to introduce light easily if natural light is not an option, because the gardening is being done in tunnels under the surface or for other reasons. The bigger challenge is water[22]. Just like humans, plants need water, so while we need plants to eat, we would be in competition with our food supply for water. Also, to complicate matters, water and oxygen act differently in Space. Without convection and thermal buoyancy, you don't get a mixing of water and air like we are used to here on Earth. These factors will make it more difficult to garden and water plants.

Speaking of watering plants, the other balance to Space gardening is you don't want astronauts to spend a large amount of time focused on it initially. In the future Space stations, the Moon and Mars are likely to have people whose full-time job is to work as a Space farmer.

[*This seems like the perfect place for a visual based off of Grant Woods 1930 iconic painting American Gothic, but the editors said that it would have multiple potential copyright issues so we have left it out of this version but if you have your own artistic interpretation of the Space farmer of 2030 please send it to us at @MilkyWayEconomy on Twitter and we would love to share some of them next time.*]

Space farmers will also be part researchers, as it has already been studied that shoots grow in various new and interesting directions based on where

---

[22] Worth noting here is that we do not do a very good job at the transportation of water here on Earth. Also, besides sugars, oils, nuts, raisins, butter and pepperoni the majority of your diet is foods that are made up of 25% or more water. Foods like milk, fruit, vegetables and most meats are 50% of more water. That additional weight from water and the transportation of that water is a major part of supply chains. Also, worldwide it is estimated that 200 million hours are spent yearly by, mostly, women and girls collecting water. Water is an example of an Earth problem that solutions we come up with to solve for Space could positively impact millions here.

you place nutrients and light. Given that Space farming will undoubtedly provide some very unique placement possibilities of nutrients and light, this is an entire field of potential study. This is also fascination because it would allow for examination of the communication system used by plants to regulate growth, interact and adapt to habitats. This process is not well understood and operates completely differently from what we see with animals using a central nervous system and brain. Spoiler alert, if you have not seen the movie *The Happening* with Mark Walberg, I am going to spoil it for you, plants can talk to each other and they don't like humans. This plant communication system is also part of the basis for the "Tree of Souls" in James Cameron's *Avatar*, where the plants do like humans enough to provide a USB port for the hero's spirit to upload into a new body. While both of these examples are Sci-Fi, as we have already learned, it is the imagination of that powerful genre that has led to the innovation of countless advancements in Space technology. The study of the communication mechanism of plants seems fertile ground to plant a stake in for a target of future research and breakthroughs. Also, as an overarching theme, the promotion of pure science, research and development and its important benefits cannot be overstated. For example, when you invent waterproof tape for ammo boxes you have no way of knowing it ends up as the essential handyman tool Duct Tape. Or when you build portable ventilator technology at NASA that leads to the portable medical 731s used in hospital admissions and military ops.

Chapter 46 - Urban Farming and CRISPR Lessons

Space farmers in the more immediate future will be focused on production capabilities that they can bring with them from farmtech and current urban growing operations. Current urban farming operations already use lots of advanced technology and specialized systems to regulate the quantities of fresh vegetables and herbs on site. The initial firms that specialize in this area of the Space economy will serve as a piece in the supply chain to augment but not replace the food being brought up to astronauts. The idea here is to alleviate some of the transportation costs of elevating all the food required by having some plants that can grow in dedicated areas on Space stations or the Moon.

The plants in Space are also likely to be highly specialized and even genetically modified by techniques like CRISPR gene editing technology. The potential role of genetic engineering and gene editing for the Space economy could be an entire chapter, or book some other time, but for now it is important to appreciate it as another Fourth Industrial Revolution technology that will be applied to the Fifth Industrial Revolution in Space. GMO (genetically modified organisms) Space plants would not need to have as many leaves, which is biomass that can traditionally not be consumed by people. Also, the plants would benefit from being capable of greater photosynthesis, minimizing size and resource needs and enhanced food production. The modification of increasing photosynthesis activity would allow the plants to produce both more oxygen for the Space farmers and convert more carbon dioxide into food.

So far lettuce, cucumbers, bok choy, rice, beans, corn, cabbage, mustard, red kale, and other plants have been involved with hundreds of experiments conducted in Space. Many of these experiments have taken place on the ISS, where researchers were able to eat some of the plants afterwards. Another important contributor to the work is the Buzz Aldrin Space Institute. Experimenting with Hawaiian volcanic soil, similar to what is found on Mars, is also part of a Martian gardens program aimed at helping NASA figure out best practices for growing plants on future missions to the red planet. As recently as 2017, an advanced greenhouse called the Advanced Plant Habitat (APH) went up to the ISS with the hope of conducting even more advanced research on growing plants in Space.

The first thing that future Space Green Thumbs will need to know is that the ground underneath your feet on the Moon or Mars is not soil, it is regolith. Soil is different from regolith in that it has been acted on by a biological agent, think enzymes, plants, bugs and worms. By comparison, regolith is just crushed up volcanic rock and dust, and doesn't have any of the critical biological agents in it that soil does. Regolith is difficult to work with because it also has a tendency to compact because of how fine it is, and when wet, turns into a clay-like material. As any gardener knows, clay is not great for plants because it can prevent both oxygen and water from reaching the roots. An interesting possible solution is to use 3D-printed nylon out of materials found on the Moon or Mars to separate the regolith, or the nylon itself could be used as a growing surface. Squash, mellons, cucumbers, beans, tomatoes and many other plants do very well growing up and along netting with limited contact to soil.

Trendy Micogreens Salads with Tabasco Dressing

According to NASA, the number one most asked for food when astronauts return to Earth is not a fat juicy cheeseburger or a medium rare steak, it's a giant salad. This might have something to do with the NASA astronaut screening process that needs to be examined or it could be a reflection on just how powerful an urge most healthy people have to eating vegetables. Either way, astronauts, Space tourists, and colonists are all in luck because those salads in Space will be put together in as trendy a style as what you might find in your favorite restaurant. It was chefs who originally looked to microgreens as a novel way to increase the color and flavor of garnishes and salads, and since that time microgreens have seen a huge surge in popularity.

What makes microgreens in the Space economy so interesting is that the movement has also started an explosion of entrepreneurs who engage in vertical and indoor closed space gardening to supply demand. This is all done with very little water and low light. Microgreens can grow in only a week to three weeks, which is much shorter than the time it takes to grow lettuce, kale, or other common salad bases, so it makes for a quick turnaround from plant to harvest. At the time microgreens are harvested, they are generally only 1 to 3 inches tall (3 to 8 cm), which makes them ideal for compact areas. Since space in Space is so valuable, this is also important because it cuts down on greenhouse space on a spacecraft, and again, since we are talking about so many thousands of dollars per kilogram, every bit of weight taken up by seeds and facilities counts. This is a balancing act because the big benefit of traditional vegetables[23] is that you can cut/pick them and get multiple harvests out of the same plants but many microgreens don't regrow after harvest (peas are an exception); so you need to bring a lot of small seeds. This leaves room in Space farming for a bit of both types of plants in the diets of astronauts.

The other reason for microgreens in Space diets is they have a stronger taste and a bright color; two things absent in many other foods off Earth. A variety of vegetables and herbs such as lettuce, radish, beets, cabbage, celery and kale are all edible, pack a significant punch of flavor, and are well purposed for microgreen growing. . That is one of the reasons that Tabasco sauce and shrimp with cocktail sauce are so popular among astronauts. When on the ISS, your body's fluids go all over the place because they are not subject to gravity, creating a congestive effect on your nasal passages thereby impacting your ability to taste and enjoy food. This effect is well studied but with differing gravities of new commercial space stations, the Moon and Mars are also likely to play a similar effect on eating depending on the amount of gravity.

---

[23] This is also the case with cherry tomatoes, which are a fruit, and something that does exceedingly well for my children in their garden. Please, if you need any let me know!

Tabasco, ketchup, and ranch will all be very popular condiments in luxury space hotel restaurants. It turns out that unlike blockchain, you can put hot sauce on everything, at least in Space. Really the impact on taste buds is intuitive when we think about how things taste different on airplanes. Taste matters not only because you want people to enjoy themselves, but you also need people to want to eat the food you are making them grow and consume. Chinese cabbage is a current flavor-ranking winner based on several space taste testing rounds, so entrepreneurial cooks up for the challenge should start experimenting with it now for recipes.

Microgreens are also packed with nutrition often with 5-times as many vitamins and antioxidants than adult plants. Antioxidants in Space are very important as they are known to help prevent cell damage here on Earth. This is before any efforts that are likely to be applied to enhance vitamins with DNA or synthetic biology techniques of microgreens. Chinese cabbage (Bok Choy and Napa) red cabbage, giant mustard, bacon radish all can contribute to monthly biomass for astronaut food.

The first step in growing microgreens or plants of any kind is the addition of nutrients to regolith, and one of the ways being looked at to do that is urine. Scientists have already been hard at work mixing Moon regolith with urine, and it turns out it is a great activation and fertilizer agent.

Chapter 47 - Circular Economics of Space Pee

What is interesting about this experiment with regolith and urine from the standpoint of an economist is; given the necessity of having food supplies grown in Space and the prohibitive cost associated with sending up Earth soil, it becomes obvious that urine would have tremendous value. The urine itself could be used for irrigation, but process urea components could also be used for the valuable nitrogen from the ammonia as well as carbon and metabolic wastes. This would be a valuable resource on space stations, and for early colonization efforts for the Moon and Mars, to transform regolith into usable inputs to Space gardens.

Given the value of each of these component parts pee will feed into a system that is as efficient as possible. A great example of efficient, low water, and high output systems are Pure Harvest Smart Farms. They are a UAE based startup that operates greenhouses 7-times more efficient than their competitors, and 30-times more efficient than traditional field farming. Also, the advanced farmtech being used by the company allows them to turn 83% of the water they consume into food when it leaves the farms. With these types of outputs on Earth already happening, an extension of these technologies for Space technologies seems perfectly within our grasp.

In addition to not wanting to waste them the other interesting thing about valuable resources is that they tend to have markets created around them. This could mean that one of the first and most actively traded markets in the Space Economy could be urea. The other potential is for alternative and novel systems of circular economics to develop where bottled water is cheap, but that is only so that the space station can collect and process larger amounts of urine for recycling into valuable fertilizer. The economics of recycling in Space, especially for certain Earth products that have valuable component parts, is fascinating to think through more. It is entirely possible that certain items brought into Space get more valuable as recycled component materials the farther away from Earth we get. A system where component parts and a need to recycle and reuse those parts has a higher demand than the original finished product will have interesting economic consequences and lead to the development of intense and targeted recycling programs.

Chapter 48 - Zero-G Fish Farms

Since not everyone in Space is going to want to go Vegan, another option is aquaculture. In a contained system, water could be used for aquaponics, growing vegetables while fish simultaneously live in the water system. Fish inside water are already suspended, so the impact of microgravity is considerably less. Also, you have the option of spinning the tanks to apply a small amount of artificial gravity to them. But in the absence of gravity, some fish have been shown to swim in loops but soon adapt to Zero-G, while other fish have been shown to just lay still. In both cases, as long as access to food is provided, the lack of Earth's gravity doesn't appear to be a major issue for fish. Fish experiments have been going on in Space since the 1970s, and it is a fascinating body of research.

Also, another way the tanks for fish could work is based off some of the early Transhab concepts of inflatable space modules for increasing living area in Space. The concept of the design is to include water layers as radiation shielding, so introducing fish to these layers is a natural next step in the technology. If this seems a bit farfetched keep in mind that on Earth, we have already been raising many different fish species for decades on completely landlocked, close loop commercial aquaculture systems, so why couldn't we do it "spacelocked"? The idea also is that what works for a Space station or longer duration mission into Space or colony on the Moon or Mars will not be the same. Just as it is true with some of the other topics discussed for 3D-printing and Urban farming, it is likely that while overarching lessons will be learned, each of these unique environments will have variations on the systems that are needed to successfully and economically produce food.

Tilapia is a very popular fish and it has been previously cryopreserved, so not only is it a desirable source of protein (and tasty), its fingerlings are small and the tools to fertilize new batches can be easily stored. Fingerlings are the tiny baby Tilapia of which thousands at a time could be kept in a single liter bottle of water. Also interesting is that Tilapia fingerlings will naturally regulate their growth rate when the water is kept cold, feed is limited, and they are packed in at high densities. Tilapia has also been popularly used in small-scale aquaculture production for years with proven technology and techniques on Earth that could be adapted for application in Space. They are healthy to consume and good feeders that prefer a diet of algae. Tilapia, and fish in general, feeding on only algae are generally very high in Omega-3 fatty acids, and while this is healthy, it makes the fish oily and less desirable for food consumption, so also including corn, soy, or processed food wastes into their diets is a possible technique. The diet of the fish is also important because some commonly consumed fish eat other fish, which could complicate the operations in Space. Think of the set up like a scaled aquaculture system or Ecosphere. Where a self-contained system with fish and snails feeding plants, and plants feeding fish and snails and astronauts eating small quantities of both which requires minimal maintenance, other than having to add more water, nutrients and new plant seeds on occasion. Balancing, perfecting and commercializing larger versions of this system will be a multi-Billion-dollar business for some company in the Space economy.

Chapter 49 - The Anatomy of a $1000 Burger

The economics of people willing to pay premium prices for meat in space, because it is so rare, should factor into the designs of future habitats. Mega satellites fashioned into cutting edge research Space labs in the future will need to keep workers happy and engaged. There are enormous positive psychological impacts of having a tasty and satisfying meal at the end of a long day of work. Rewarding people who work hard all day with delicious food is important to the success of firms and operations in Space to maintain workforce health and productivity. It is one of the reasons that NASA has a major kitchen operation and why as other firms operate more in Space they will also be concerned with food in orbit.

These mental benefits a lso also extend to providing a feeling of home for astronauts and is why flowers have also been present on the ISS. Tending and caring for something external to self is good for the mental health of crew members. Also, a "walkabout", as described in traditional Australian Aboriginal culture, and the Japanese practice of "forest bathing" [shinrin-yoku], have been shown to provide benefits to the psyche of people here on Earth. The good news is that larger commercial operations of farming in Space could also rent out time for mental health walks to people in need of being surrounded by greenspaces.

More immediately, the time spent close-up with plants harvesting crops to eat may provide some of these same psychological benefits in dedicated modules on space stations, the Moon or long duration journeys to Mars. Keeping people anchored mentally in the weightlessness of Space is critical to mission accomplishment.

Cows are Heavy and Space Hamburgers are Expensive

Cows are heavy and stress out easily. The first point might be obvious, but it is worth repeating, and as far as the second point you will have to take my word for it as someone who grew up on farms and around animals. Cows are also not useful as a food source in the same way that plants are. You cannot simply pick and eat a cow like you do a plant crop with no cooking and limited messy cleanup. Also, cows are competition when it comes to oxygen while plants on the other hand help recycle the carbon dioxide, we omit back into oxygen for us to breathe.

If you can't send cows up into Space, then that means the price of a hamburger, meatball, or steak will be astronomically high on space stations, the Moon, or Mars. To dig into this a bit more (as a huge lover of a good steak and burgers) let's just start with the simplifying assumption that the cost of getting foodstuffs to where you're living in Space is about $1000/kg. Since 1kg is about 35oz and a good beef patty is about 6-to-7oz let's just say it works out to about 6 per kg, thus putting the cost of just the patty at $170. Next, we have to consider how we are going to cook it. You are not going to fire up a grill in Space, but assuming you solve for that you are still going to want something to go with your Space beef patty. If this isn't intuitive, let's just go with fire in an air lock is bad and think of every Space movie you have seen involving a spark contacting oxygen. [*Interesting to note is, the behavior of flames is currently being studied on the ISS and previous work by NASA led to the development of several fire-retardant materials, coatings, paints, and foams, many widely used today.*] I don't see how simply using a microwave gets us to flame-grilled goodness, but science is a wonderful thing, and someone will solve for this if they haven't already.

Next, we have to consider the buns. Baking in Space is something that is both very interesting and important. Who doesn't feel better after eating a warm slice of bread? The way the warm bread absorbs the butter slathered on top, and the crust is just a bit flaky still from just coming out of the oven. [*I hope that was mildly tortuous to any of my high protein low carb diet friends.*] Interestingly, it is the flakiness of the crust and the crumbs that come along with bread that is also a big concern of astronauts, and an important factor in why currently on the ISS astronauts are forced to eat tortillas. Several firms have conducted research on baking bread and even

165

cookies in Space, which also has to overcome the challenges of not just the potential of fire, but also the effects of microgravity and finding a yeast that will work under those conditions. Not to mention the fact that, absent thermal convection to mix up air on the ISS, a super-hot pocket of air coming out of an oven would pose potential serious problems floating around the station. So, let's just assume for a minute that you can easily purchase your burger with a delicious potato bun for another $80.

Putting the price of the beef patty, the bun, and some space lettuce, onions and tomato together you are likely looking at paying $300 just on input costs, and that doesn't include cheese or condiments. Cheese also has a long history in Space, including hitching a ride on the first SpaceX space capsule orbit back in 2010. Cheese comes from milk, which also comes from cows, and as mentioned before; they don't do well in Space, so this is likely an imported good from Earth to the kitchen at the Moon Cheers preparing your burger and fries. Last you have the rest of the costs associated with the restaurant in the Space hotel. If you look at the cost structure of menu items on a typical Earth establishment, you can see that only about a third of prices are input costs, and another two thirds comes from facilities and labor. Just using these as a proxy and giving us a bit of wiggle room in our estimate, you are at almost $1,000 (2019 USD) for a burger.

If this sounds like my attempt at burgernomics it is. Readers of The Economist might be familiar with the Big Mac Index, first introduced by Pam Woodall, which seeks to provide a measurement of purchasing power parity. If not, it is an insightful tool often used by economists to compare the prices of a similar basket of goods in different locations. For the Big Mac Index, it is looking at the basket of goods used to make a McDonald's Big Mac and the cost paid in currencies in different countries for the sake of comparison. It is based on the law of one price, which is more of a concept than a law in economics that says that in a free market, absent friction, the price of the identical good must sell for the same price in different countries. Extending this a bit to Space is simple enough and applied to our estimations for the hamburger constructed above, we can see for example, that when compared to $5.67 for a Big Mac the difference is 175-times. So, does this mean that food, and by extension labor and facilities, will be 175-times more expensive in Space? Well, it provides a tool to start to think about it and to ask other questions to help frame our thinking. But what are you going to drink with your burger and fries?

Chapter 50 - Beer's Final Frontier

What goes better with a burger and fries than beer? Now we must simply admit now that we can't all be Captain Jon-Luc Picard and drink "tea earl gray hot" all the time, so it is probably better to observe moderation like Captain Mal Reynolds taught us while in Space. Alcohol in Space also has a long history outside of sci-fi. Apollo 8 had 3 bottles of brandy on board to circle the Moon. It was not intended to be consumed but was more ceremonial. It is also the case that on the Apollo 11 Moon landing before stepping out onto the lunar surface that Buzz Aldrin took Holy Communion, which includes the consumption of bread and wine as remembrance of the body and blood of Christ. While this was done as part of religious observation and mental preparation, this does mark the only person known to have consumed alcohol on another planetary body, but this is unlikely to be a record that stands for much longer.

Most Space agencies have strict policies prohibiting alcohol, and although it has been rumored that both cognac and vodka have made their way up to the ISS and MIR, beer consumption however is known to have never occurred, even though beer has been to Space. If you can name which beer before we share it I'd be very impressed. Give up? Natty Light. It was sent up nearly a decade ago by two space enthusiasts using a weather balloon, cooler, GPS, and camera. The question of consumption, or even manufacturing beer in Space, however, is another issue entirely. It is safe to say beer and alcohol will be in Space as the last 10,000 years of fermentation are not going to be left behind when humans move out away from Earth. It will be interesting to see when the first space brewery/distillery is set up and again it will be based on the economics of transportation vs building like discussed so many times previously with Space.

So, while astronauts are not likely to be the first consumers of alcoholic beverages, the workers, residents and space tourists visiting space stations, the Moon and Mars are. Budweiser (InBev) knows this and sees the economic opportunity so much that it has already conducted four different barley germination experiments in Space, which is part of its "Bud on Mars" program. This effort is important because it is not simply a bit of clever marketing, but part of an understanding of the larger role the alcohol plays in colonization. Where you have colonies, be those on the Moon or Mars, you soon have agriculture and with that comes barley for malting and beer for drinking.

The metabolization of alcohol in Space is also something science will need to explore before bar service is open to space tourists; to make sure the health implications are understood. In addition to barley for beer, experiments for wine and scotch have also been conducted on the ISS. Another big market that seems likely is Champagne in Space, or simply "champs" since it would not be originating from the region of France official champagne must come from to carry that name. It makes sense that if you are going to be paying $250,000 for a trip to a luxury space hotel, you are going to want a selfie of you drinking a glass of champagne. Humans are predictable, and this photoshoot is surely already planned by someone seeking Instagram fame. Now the thing about "champs" is, unlike wine and scotch but more like beer, you must think about the carbonation. Bubbles in Space are not like they are here under Earth's gravity and a bubble in your stomach could have real consequences not yet fully explored or appreciated. Put simply, gas goes up on Earth but in microgravity environments it will want to travel to the center and expand. I think we get what expanding gas in the stomach means without having to just come out and say it, and that doesn't sound much like a high-class luxury experience. From beans to beef, water to recycled urine, and Natty Light to champs, the room for entrepreneurs to experiment, novel economic systems around food and beverage to develop, and scientists to discover what the future of our food and alcohol consumption in Space looks like is truly wide open.

Chapter 51 - Current State of the Space Economy and AI

"Once you have an innovation culture, even those who are not scientists or engineers – poets, actors, journalists – they, as communities, embrace the meaning of what it is to be scientifically literate. They embrace the concept of an innovation culture." - Neil deGrasse Tyson

Note – this chapter is not missing. It just got redacted and not by Samson or George. We're working on AI & The Space Economy as a stand-alone book in the series. Tune back in late 2022.

Chapter 52 - Predictions for the Space Economy 2030 to 2100

Thank you for joining us for an introductory journey into The Space Economy. We'd like to summarize this book with a few bullet points and some not so crazy predictions. Feel free add to the predictions and share your feelings with us on Twitter **@MilkyWayEconomy** and be sure to use the following hashtags: #TheSpaceEconomy #SpaceEconomy #SpacePredictions. And now to summarize Blockchain & The Space Economy:

████████████████████████

2. Everything in Space runs on a Blockchain network.
3. The future of money is digital.
4. The future of currency is tokenized.
5. The future of value is Utility ElementalTokens (UETs)
6. In Space, the poor pay in gold, the wealthy pay in pomegranates.
   a. You'll understand this when your read Blockchain & The Space Economy, Chapter 38, *There is no money on Mars*.

Predictions you can bet the farm on!

2022 - NASA launches Psyche16 Asteroid probe. Psyche16 is an asteroid that is thought to be the remnants of a planet's core comprising ~$98,000,000,000,000,000,000 ($98 Quintillion) worth of precious metals. Meaning every person on earth could be a billionaire, several times.

2023 - India announces it is sending a mining probe to Psyche16 to mine a 1-mile chunk of the asteroid and steer it back into orbit near Earth.

2024 - The first American, female astronaut to walk on the moon is a Black woman.

2026 - Psyche16 probe lands and surveys the asteroid, determining its value.

2028 - With the first Indian shipment of gold ore headed back from b ack from Psyche16, the USA and China declare war on India.

2029 - Following the nuclear fallout of MAD (Mutually Assured Destruction), the Earth's population declines by ~3.5B.

2030 - Clean drinking water is now worth its weight in gold.

2034 - Elon Musk moves himself, his Board and SpaceX employees aboard the recently constructed *"BFSS One"* low orbit Earth space station.

2040 - Humanity finds the political will to address Global Warming, Climate Change, and makes the investments to push the cultural and business behavior changes needed to pivot humanity forward into a sustainable, ecologically friendly future.

2099 – Humanity has its first contact with Extraterrestrial beings, who admit they have been on Earth since 2020.

Prolog – Book IV, AI & The Space Economy

"In Space everything is automated" – Lt Colonel Aaron Celaya, Space Force, AI Liaison

Book IV in the Milky Way Economy's Space Economy Series is *AI & The Space Economy.* In this book we will explore the role that Artificial Intelligence will play in Space, from maintenance, National Security to tourism and of course, the monetization of Space data.

See you in Book IV, AI and The Space Economy! Join us as we boldly go where no Space Economist and Anthropologist have gone before (well almost). Into the uncharted region of AI, the Singularity and the future of permanent Human settlement of Space....even if those Humans are cyborgs.

Made in United States
North Haven, CT
11 June 2022

20125792R00095